BOOK OF SUCCESSFUL FIREPLACES

Tho I may state that on the whole
I am a rather sanguine soul,
I must confess that moments come
In which I feel morose and glum.
The medicine that I require
Is often just to build a fire.
For I have seldom felt alone
Where sprightly dancing flames have shone,
Assuring me their fellowship
In every facile bob and dip.

And fire is a tactful friend
Quite willing that you shall attend
The book, or tune or vagrant thought
By which your fancy has been caught.
When two converse, it makes a third
With never an interrupting word.

So partner if you feel distressed
And sad forebodings fill your breast,
I recommend that you resist
The urge for a psychiatrist.
Instead, appease your soul's desire
By kindling a cheerful fire.
Its bright salute and warm caress
May help as much and costs you less.

H. P. BOYNTON

BOOK OF SUCCESSFUL FIREPLACES

How to Build, Decorate and Use Them

19th edition

by R. J. Lytle and
Marie-Jeanne Lytle

Structures Publishing Company

Farmington, Michigan 1971

Manufactured in the United States of America

Book designed by Richard Kinney

Current Printing (last digit)
10 9 8 7 6 5 4 3 2
International Standard Book Number: 0-912336-02-1
Library of Congress Catalog Card Number: 79-166418
Structures Publishing Company
Box 423, Farmington, Mich. 48024

Jacket and Frontispiece Photos: Herrlin Studio, Barrington, Ill.
Photo on Page vii: California Redwood Association, Photo, Philip Molten

contents

Preface

Fire—the original source of heat, light and food—has been the central feature of the home since man first emerged in the dark of pre-history. Today these three central needs are met with devices sometimes as swift as the microseconds of electronics—yet fire, a living, glowing fire, is still one of the most prized features of a home.

Since the fireplace often is an important element in a new or remodeled home, there is need for a standard reference work which brings together all old and new knowledge of this subject.

This book is addressed primarily to builders, architects, remodelers, and to serious homeowners who must know what makes a fireplace successful, as well as beautiful. As in every other field of construction, there are principles which never change and new developments which are as recent as the past year.

The Donley Brothers Co., founded before the turn of the century, published this book for 50 years. In that half-century, close to a million copies were distributed and this work became a standard source of information for architects, builders and tradesmen. Men and women planning a new or remodeled home used it as a source of ideas.

The Donley Brothers Co. recently discontinued operations after three quarters of a century of service to the industry. The authors feel privileged to continue the tradition of this book.

This edition, the nineteenth, brings up to date the information now available on this important element of construction. New products and solutions to old problems are explored.

A whole volume on the history of the fireplace could be written. From the caveman days when a fire smouldered day and night in the center of the cave and smoke drifted lazily out the mouth of the natural crevice, the fireplace developed gradually into a monster of numerous openings, spits, side ovens, warming nooks, and bed nooks for humans. Then centuries of inventiveness created more efficient means of lighting—the electric light; of cooking—the range; and finally of heating—the central furnace.

For a period of years, the fireplace was in eclipse and many homes were built without them. But something was missing. Men missed the personal warmth and cheeriness of an actual fire, the sense of community and relaxation when the family or friends gathered around the hearth. So, in a sense, the demand for this feature in a home came full circle and a fireplace today is probably the most sought-after "extra" after the basic home is planned.

Only expense and a feeling that existing construction makes a fireplace impossible probably keep many people from enjoying this pleasure. Yet, as an examination of this volume will show, ingenuity has solved even these problems. With modern manufacturing techniques, a fireplace can be provided in almost any type of building, old or new. In urban areas where wood is unavailable and coal undesirable, now the homeowner can enjoy a gas or electric fireplace.

We have even gone back to one of the earliest fundamentals—cooking. The outdoor barbecue has moved inside so that the family can enjoy its favorite open fire foods year-round.

In essence, there are three major factors to be considered in building a fireplace—simple success as a construction feature (there is no pleasure in a fireplace that smokes or gives out little heat), safety, and design.

In these pages, we give you the construction principles which assure that a fireplace will operate satisfactorily. We underline over and over the safety features which must be built into your fireplace, whether custom-built or pre-built by manufacturing techniques.

And lastly, we present through photographs and text the infinite variety of design now available for the fireplace, from traditional through the most contemporary, and the ways in which this age-old convenience can become the very center of a happy home.

*Let my glowing embers warm your hearts to all
the world.
Light your fire and never fear,
Life was made for love and cheer.*
— HENRY VAN DYKE: "The Hearthstone."

A home without a fireplace does seem to lack something—a certain something that is the heart of the home. It is true that we no longer need a fireplace in each room in order to survive the cold of the winter. There is an element of security, however, in knowing that you could have a fire if necessary. The pioneer spirit still lives within us.

Although fireplaces are no longer necessary for survival, a working fireplace with a cheerful fire blazing away exudes an atmosphere of happy congenial living and contributes to the feeling that this is the good life! Even during the hot summer months, the mind envisions the image of a crackling fire and enjoys the atmosphere of hospitality, rest and repose that is in the mind's eye. A fireplace suggests the comfort and contentment of quiet evenings before a blazing hearth.

Before we go on more deeply into the planning and building of a fireplace, let us first of all remember this good rule: "Never lose sight of the fact that the most important factor of a fireplace is the fire itself." In following this rule, this means that the designer of the fireplace must stay with a relatively simple fireplace, installed at moderate costs on well-tested principles and using locally available materials.

Need of Right Construction

A common evil exists in the vast number of faultily constructed fireplaces whose owners and builder intended that they should provide a measure of fireside satisfaction, but which fail to do so through faulty construction. This may result from ignorance or inattention at a time when the owner is occupied with other features of his home project. It may reflect somebody's mistaken effort to hold down costs, or from mere absence of suitable plans to crystallize the intentions and to guide against errors of construction.

Easy To Be Right

It is almost as easy to build a successful fireplace as to build a bad one. Certain principles must be observed. Those principles are embodied in the drawings and directions to be found in ensuing chapters.

Besides these positive guides, attention may well be

given to Chapter 11 where common mistakes are pointed out and discussed.

The fireplace you are entitled to have for your money invested is a fireplace in which fires are kindled readily, burn smoothly, yield generous heat, and discharge smoke and gases *up* the flue.

It is the purpose of this book to help you in solving the problems that confront anyone looking forward to the ownership of a fireplace, whether in a home to be built or an interior to be remodeled.

This chapter begins by mentioning the different types of fireplaces, the important features of each to assist in a reasonable choice. Later chapters will explain in detail the necessary instructions for success with each type.

Types of Fireplaces

One of the major decisions that you will have to make with your family is "what type of fireplace?" If you have the space and can afford it, you will probably choose the ever popular masonry fireplace. Desire for heat from the fireplace may lead to a heat circulating fireplace. Need for economy may dictate a prebuilt fireplace of the built in type or freestanding metal. A remodeling project may suggest a prebuilt, gas, or electric fireplace.

The Conventional Masonry Fireplace

A wide range of styles and types of masonry fireplaces have developed over the years. Beyond the traditional fireplace in the wall there are corner fireplaces in both exterior and interior corners; fireplaces in which the flame is visible in two or three directions; double opening fireplaces that serve two rooms on opposite sides of a partition wall, and hooded fireplaces.

Heat Circulating Fireplaces

This is another general type of fireplace which gives you more heat for your fuel than the masonry fireplace. A circulator, like a furnace, gives you the bonus of the circulated, convection heated air. This type of fireplace is most useful in a vacation cottage which has no furnace, or in a home where warmth is needed between the seasons but turning on the heat is not quite justified.

The mellow brick fireplace is a strong architectural element in this beautiful interior. Note the interesting interplay of lines, planes, colors and textures. (Herrlin Studio, photo.)

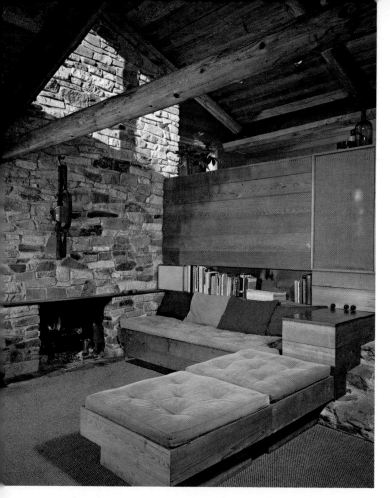

Exciting combination of textures and interesting built-in seating form an inviting fireplace. (Charles R. Pearson, photo.)

Massive carved stone fireplace provides an interesting setting for a glowing fire at the end of the day. (Louis Reens, photo.)

Pre-Built Fireplaces

Although masonry fireplaces are most often preferred, they are not always possible for everyone. The pre-built fireplace offers excellent solutions to various problems. A pre-built makes it possible to install a woodburning fireplace without concrete footings, without a masonry chimney, at lower cost, and in a room where structural considerations would otherwise rule out a fireplace. The pre-built is a great boon to apartment dwellers, vacation home builders, and to folks remodeling their home or adding on a room.

There are two basic types of pre-built fireplaces; the "built in pre-built," which is a conventional appearing fireplace usually built into a wall, and the metal fireplace, usually freestanding.

The *built in pre-built* fireplace is usually built into a conventional setting with a brick or woodpaneled wall and with a slate, tile, or other hearth. It is difficult to identify as metal or pre-built. The metal fireplace, on the other hand, is obviously and attractively metal, with striking and unusual shapes available. Most metal fireplaces are quite modern with one important exception—the ever popular Franklin stove. Metal fireplaces come not only in a variety of shapes, but also in a rainbow of colors and materials. They can be made of black wrought iron, copper and many gorgeous colors of easy-to-clean porcelain on steel.

Electric and Gas Fireplaces

If it is not possible to have a wood- or coal-burning fireplace where you live, or you do not want to go through the mess of a solid fuel fire, and yet you crave the warmth and glow of a fire, do not despair—there is a solution! There are electric or gas fireplaces for low cost which give you the glow of the fire with no mess, and the added advantage of quick response—an instant cozy fire. The gas fireplace needs a vent but this is easily and economically installed.

Various Rooms

It is a happy home that has a single living room fireplace, even if cost or architectural restrictions make it difficult to have this feature in any other room.

However, there are other locations for a fireplace besides the living room. One that comes readily to mind is a kitchen located in the rear of the living room. Here, employing the same chimney, a cooking type of fireplace may logically be provided. It may be supplemented by gas or electric appliances in the same masonry installation.

The basement recreation room or the family room are places where many owners find joy in the presence of a fireplace, either for warmth or casual cookery or both.

A library, study, or den—the personal room of studious individuals—gains charm from an open fire.

Bedroom fireplaces are less common than in days when open fires were the chief means of warming a house. Nevertheless, there are men and women today who like to

The gleaming copper hood, raised hearth and mellow used-brick fireplace front combine to make this inglenook a cozy gathering place. (Gordon Findley, AID, and Douglas B. Kohler, AID, designers. Hedrich-Blessing, photo.)

Furniture placement around the fireplace in this elegant interior creates a sophisticated spot for after dinner relaxing. Note interesting assymetrical arrangement of accessories over classical wood mantel. (Interior design, David Russ. Hedrich-Blessing, photo.)

A cheerful hearth in the kitchen makes the tasks lighter and can take over part of the cooking, too! (Heatilator Fireplaces)

(below) A cozy evening by the hearth! Notice the well accessorized fireplace and mantel in this restful pine-paneled room. (Architect, Ralph C. Huszagh. Hedrich-Blessing, photo.)

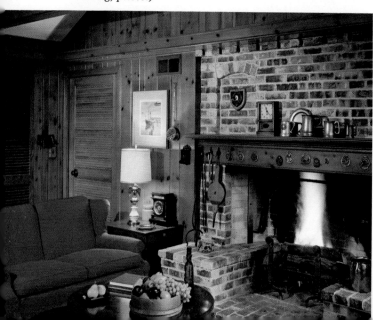

(left) A pre-built metal fireplace in an interesting two-way projecting corner installation. The fire is visible all around the corner. Notice the well chosen fireplace accessories. (Heatilator Fireplaces)

dress and undress before an open fire—to lapse into slumber while a dying fire flickers its warmth.

Office & Club

A physician whose waiting room contained a shielded and unused fireplace of a past era tells how he noted a better spirit in his patients after the fireplace was restored to use.

A club lounge or church reception room with an open fire promotes harmony of spirit.

There are many company offices in which a fireplace exerts a harmonizing influence in executive decisions or in conference deliberations.

In any of the situations discussed, the presence of a fireplace adds gracious dignity and prestige, as well as physical comfort and sociability.

Flush or Projecting

A decision must be made between having the fireplace flush with the face of the wall or projected, wholly or partly, within the room. Several factors of planning are involved, including the treatment of the exterior of the chimney, in some cases. In others, it will be features of an adjacent room that determines the choice, perhaps kitchen cooking appliances that are vented into the same stack.

Reasons for projection into the room may be the desire to flank the fireplace with cabinets or shelving to hold books or ornaments. In the case of circulator fireplaces, there is the advantage of having hot air vents installed at the side of the projection, hence making them less conspicuous than when located in the face of the upper wall.

Satisfaction Through Simplicity

We have discussed the various types of fireplaces and a few considerations governing the choice of the proper fireplace in order to give you a feel for the field as a whole. You'll be on surest ground, however, if your personal choice is for a relatively simple fireplace, installed at moderate costs on well-tested principles and using readily obtainable materials.

Above all, remember that the most important factor in any fireplace is the fire—flame has the same quality in a simple, low-cost fireplace as in the most elaborate structure.

(opposite) This attractive Early American setting extends a warm invitation to come in and have a cup of punch by the fire. Note the placement of the portraits and other accessories over the mantel. (Louis Reens, photo.)

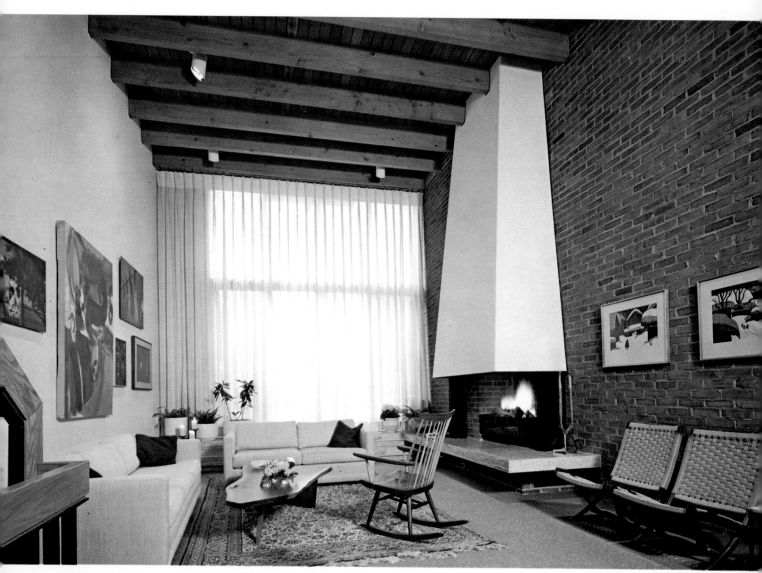

*In the remodeling of this residence, an unusual raised
hearth of Temple Cream Travertine marble was used. The
dominant ceiling-high hood and attractive seating arrangement combine to create a congenial atmosphere.
(Marble Institute of America)*

This elegant fireplace wall was created with "travel panels". Panels framed with wood moulding were painted to simulate Colonial paneling in this remodeled living room. (Western Wood Moulding)

The quiet placement of this fireplace in the wood paneled wall gives it understated importance in a comfortable interior. (Gordon Findley, AID, and Douglas B. Kohler, AID, designers. Hedrich-Blessing, photo.)

Soaring window and mellow wood walls create a striking interior. Just the sight of the hearth on a late summer's day can recall the joys of the crackling hearth. (Western Wood Products)

The soft gleam of etched metal against used brick is particularly pleasing in this hooded fireplace. Design creates an almost free-standing fireplace and adds quiet drama to this serene setting. (Charles R. Pearson, photo.)

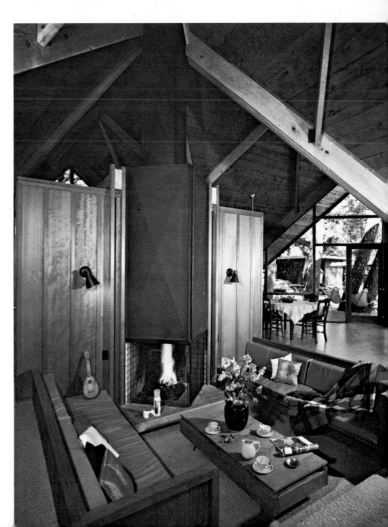

The projecting beams on either side of the fireplace extend up and over across the ceiling and focus attention to the fire in this quiet living room. (Heatilator Fireplaces)

The striking black metal hood and flue of this custom designed fireplace soars up to the center of the wood-framed roof. The sunken conversation area with comfortable built-in seating creates a most attractive and relaxing focal area for this vacation cabin. (California Redwood Association)

Free standing fireplace in ski lodge creates atmosphere of warmth and congeniality. (Malm Fireplaces— Kodak, photo.)

Free-standing porcelain-enameled metal fireplace creates a congenial area for this sophisticated apartment interior. (Majestic)

A spectacular black metal fireplace in the round designed by the owner of this ski cottage. Notice the custom-built hexagonal warming bench and the comfortable seating arrangement which also repeats the shape of the hood. A wonderful place to gather for warming up après ski. (Henry Glass, designer; Herrlin Studio, photo.)

A crackling fire, the mellow wood mantel decorated with evergreens, the gifts gayly wrapped and ready—Merry Christmas! (H. Armstrong Roberts, photo.)

A classic example of a roaring fire in a comfortable sportsman's retreat. The massive stone fireplace and thick wood mantel against the rough paneled walls are masculine without a doubt! (H. Armstrong Roberts, photo.)

Clean lines and good design result in fine example of wood storage under the fireplace. (Heatilator Fireplaces)

Electric fireplace can be moved as a unit to provide a warm Early American hearth where no other fireplace is possible. (Readybuilt)

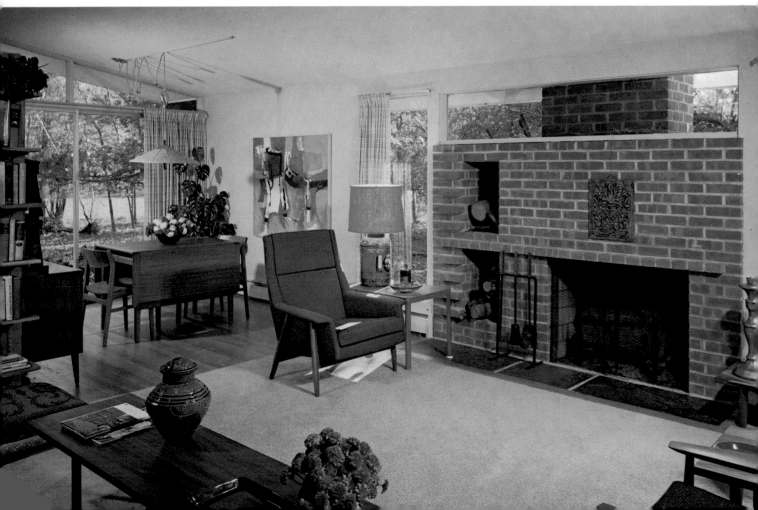

(opposite)
A fine example of a simple hooded fireplace with wood storage space under the raised hearth. The strong architectural lines of the beams and windows focus attention on the brick fireplace wall. (U.S. Gypsum Research Village; Harris Armstrong, AIA, architect. Hedrich-Blessing, photo.)

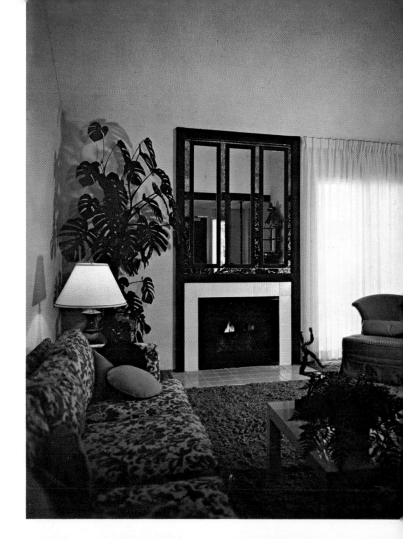

This is an unusual and extremely decorative mirrored treatment of the fireplace front. (Heatilator Fireplaces)

Free standing fieldstone fireplace with cantilevered hearth lends drama to this ski cabin, as well as warmth. The stone is particularly suited to the rough paneling and massive beams. (Western Wood Products Association)

(opposite)
An interesting design that gives a free-standing feeling to the large brick fireplace. Note the good wood storage provided and the drama of the chimney viewed through the window. (C.R. Sykora, designer. Hedrich-Blessing, photo.)

(opposite)
This well designed contemporary two-way fireplace provides warmth and a view of the flames for both living and dining areas. The white painted brick fireplace also forms a divider between them. (Hedrich-Blessing, photo.)

Black metal free standing fireplace brings a crackling woodburning fire to this vacation home. (Majestic Fireplaces)

Here the fireplace has been incorporated into the bookcase wall. Notice the beautiful simplicity and good proportions of the design of the wall as a whole. (Olaf Hammarstrom, AIA, architect. Hedrich-Blessing, photo.)

(opposite)
Straight sleek lines of this black metal hood contrasted against the rough masonry in the fieldstone fireplace wall. An interesting example of traditional materials in a modern interior. (Architect, Binkley Associates. Hedrich-Blessing, photo.)

(opposite)
A pleasant setting for cozy family dining before the open fire. Note interesting arrangement of objects around mantel. (A Scholz Home. Hedrich-Blessing, photo.)

A warm welcome in a cozy setting! The good proportions and clean lines of the Early American wood mantel combine with the gleaming brass andirons and grate to make a really cozy corner. (Photographed at Greenfield Village. Hedrich-Blessing, photo.)

Ceramic tile on fireplace wall and a ceramic floor tile create an unusual and attractive interior. (Architect, Garber, Tweddell & Wheeler. Hedrich-Blessing, photo.)

(opposite)
Rich color of redwood walls and marble mantel and hearth are a fine background for the oriental rugs and tones of upholstery in this elegant living room. Note excellent proportions of fireplace in window wall. (California Redwood Association)

27

*Black stack and powerful design of this projecting brick
fireplace provide a focal point for this contemporary living
room. (Molitor, photo.)*

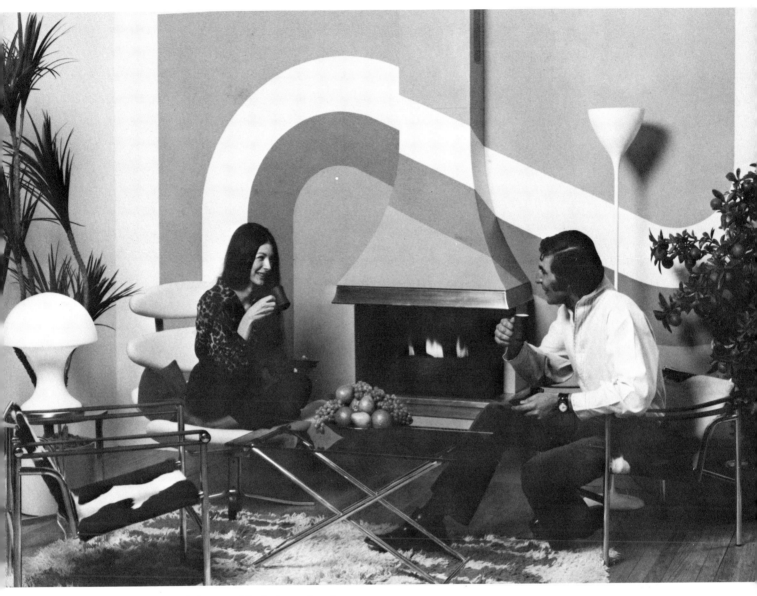

Whimsical in concept, this striking graphic design painted on wall and wall-hung metal fireplace creates a fireplace wall of great impact in an otherwise featureless corner. (Heatilator Fireplaces)

A spectacular fireplace in a tri-level setting creates a comfortable place to sit by the fire. Notice the feeling of warmth from the mellow hand-made tiles, exposed beams, and color of the walls in the fireplace area. (Pre-Built by Majestic)

2. PLANNING YOUR FIREPLACE

Location, Size, Style,
Wood Storage,
Furniture Arrangement

Location Within a Room

The foremost consideration in locating the fireplace within a room is the creation of an area of comfort and repose. Needed are plenty of room for comfortable seating, and space for whatever other fireside pleasures you contemplate, such as reading, listening to music, cooking, etc. Such space is most likely to be found at the side or end of a room. The end position is very likely to be preferable on the grounds of seclusion.

In choosing the location for your fireplace, consider the traffic pattern that will evolve. Avoid placing the fireplace where traffic from door to door passes through the room between furniture and fireplace. Please consider here, also, the poor fire tender who should not be forced to trample over guests or dodge furniture when he brings in a load of fuel from the storage area.

Structural considerations in the location of the chimney will influence the placement of the fireplace. Factors that might affect the drawing capacity of the chimney and

Poor planning! Traffic is encouraged to move between fireplace and furniture grouping.

possible down-drafts are tall trees, nearby buildings, even high ground or other topographic peculiarities of the site. If you are planning to use a single chimney (separate flues, of course!) to vent the fireplace in the living room, one in the bedroom and the furnace; this will pretty well determine your fireplace location for you. You may also plan to add an outside fireplace later on off the patio and have only one or two possible patio sites.

If your house is to be built with brick rather than wood siding, it is possible to save money on brick by placing the fireplace on an outside wall. The foundation on the outside walls is already there, whereas an inside location may require more foundation. On the other hand, common brick can be used on the concealed portions of the inside fireplace, rather than expensive face brick. Anchorage (Chapter 5) is not required on chimneys wholly within the house in those areas subject to earthquake damage. Remember, too, that an inside fireplace takes up square footage in the house, while a fireplace on an outside wall does not.

Size of the Fireplace

Now, how do you go about deciding how big a fireplace, or rather fireplace opening, to have? First of all, a word of caution to over-enthusiastic fireplace buffs—A "great big fire" in a "great big fireplace" will probably drive you from the room! On the other hand, a small fire in a large fireplace heats inefficiently and is less aesthetically appealing.

The Fireplace Opening

What we present here are certain principles that can be applied to the determination of the size of your fireplace. The main principle involved is that of fireplace "thermodynamics." There is much greater heating efficiency in a firebox thirty inches wide, well filled with flame, than there is in the same fire built in a forty-eight-inch firebox. Heat radiated from a fireplace comes, to a large extent, from the heated brickwork that surrounds the flame. Since radiant heat travels in straight lines, its effective range is limited. Therefore, plan no larger fire than the room requires, and plan the fireplace to fit the fire snugly, for maximum warmth and efficient fuel consumption.

Massive fieldstone fireplace goes beyond the glass wall and ties in the mountain view. Furniture is grouped to complement both the view and the fireplace. (Williams & Williams, Architects; Julius Shulman, photo.)

Another principle, that of good design, requires that the size of the fireplace fit the size of the room. A fireplace that is scaled too large or too small in proportion to the size of the room is visually disturbing. Here is a table of suggested widths for fireplace openings appropriate to the size of the room.

Size of Room in Feet	Width of Fireplace Opening in Inches	
	in Short Wall	in Long Wall
10 × 14	24	24 to 32
12 × 16	28 to 36	32 to 36
12 × 20	32 to 36	36 to 40
12 × 24	32 to 36	36 to 48
14 × 28	32 to 40	40 to 48
16 × 30	36 to 40	48 to 60
20 × 36	40 to 48	48 to 72

The height of the fireplace opening is usually from two-thirds to three-quarters of the width. In the end,

however, you must rely on your own good judgment.

Another factor to consider is the conventional wood fuel sizes available in your area. If you are going to use full-length four-foot cordwood, for example, the proportions of your fireplace will differ from one suited for half-length cordwood.

Style of Fireplaces

In planning your fireplace, one of the early considerations you must have is that of the main styles of fireplace and, out of these, which one will suit you best. By style, we are referring to the construction of the fireplace and its orientation to the room or rooms involved, not any architectural style. These main styles include the wall fireplace, the back-to-back fireplace, the corner fireplace, the two-way fireplace (through wall), the three-way fireplace, the hooded fireplace, and the free standing fireplace.

Back-to-back design economizes on masonry costs.

Fireplace on an inside corner with appropriate furniture arrangement.

The Wall Fireplace is the most conventional style, of course, and the most frequently built. This style may incorporate the whole wall in its design or may be a small, but dominating part of the design of the wall as a whole. Whenever possible, a wood pass-through or wood storage box should be provided.

A Back-to-Back design permits the use of the same masonry mass for two fireplaces. This is a great cost saver when there are two rooms with a common wall such as a family room and living room or patio for an outdoor fireplace and living room. However, even though two fireplaces use the same chimney, each must have a separate flue.

Corner Fireplaces are of two types, inside corner and outside or projecting corner. They can be used for excellent room dividers with less danger of smoking in a cross draft.

Two-Way Fireplaces have two opposite faces or two opposite fire openings. This style of fireplace serves as an excellent room divider and spreads its heat to both rooms on either side. Two-way, three-way, hooded, and free standing fireplaces each present separate technical problems which should be solved by the damper manufacturer.

Two-way fireplace serves as excellent room divider and spreads heat and cheer to both rooms.

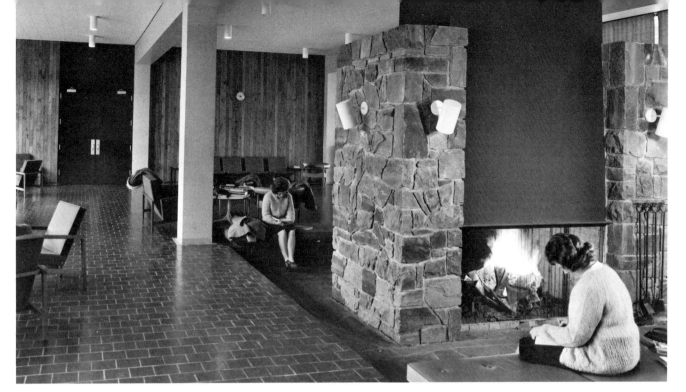

Student building has fireplace with metal hood, sunken hearth. (Joseph Molitor, photo.)

A Three-Way Fireplace is like a peninsula, opening on three adjacent open sides and is a style that also serves as an excellent room divider, and can be very dramatic, with the fire visible on three sides.

The Hooded Fireplace (usually with metal hood) is becoming very popular and is both dramatic and efficient. It is efficient because the metal hood is heated and gives off heat both by radiation and convection. A hooded fireplace is often less complicated to construct than the conventional form, as it sometimes permits the elimination of heavy chimney work and foundation masonry (building codes permitting). The metal hood may be of different metals (sheet iron finished in charcoal black or shiny copper, for example) and of many different designs. The hood can increase the effectiveness of the fireplace by radiating heat when it warms up, as well as adding a striking decorative touch to the room.

Three-way fireplace, wood box, and kitchen barbecue are all on one masonry wall.

Contemporary two-way fireplace gives both living and dining rooms a view of the flames. (Hedrich-Blessing, photo.)

33

Ideal furniture grouping for this free standing fireplace.
(Lawrence Williams, photo.)

Free Standing Fireplaces are sometimes built on the same specifications as the hooded fireplaces above, but more often they are metal fireplaces as described in Chapter 7. This type of fireplace permits complete freedom from the wall and allows seating all around.

Wood Storage

In planning, consider also the practicality of providing for nearby wood storage. There are many ways to provide for fuel storage in a fireplace plan. A good arrangement is a fireside locker with a door that opens outside or into the garage. The wood cabinet can be integrated into the over-

all design of the fireplace wall. A recess can be planned in the fireplace wall for wood storage or the wood can be stacked under a raised hearth. The sight of a good supply of wood gives a sense of security and promise of long and enjoyable fires.

Furniture Placement

There are a few general principles to remember in planning the placement of furniture around the fireplace. The main goal to keep in mind is a restful grouping of seating and tables with the fireplace as the center of interest.

Ideally the area in front of or around the hearth could be a sunken conversation pit, but, of course, this cannot

Restful furniture grouping with fireplace as center of interest.

Wood storage under fireplace (Heatilator Fireplaces)

Masonry wall with fireplace and wood pass-through

Sunken conversation pit simplifies furniture arrangement. (Joseph Molitor, photo.)

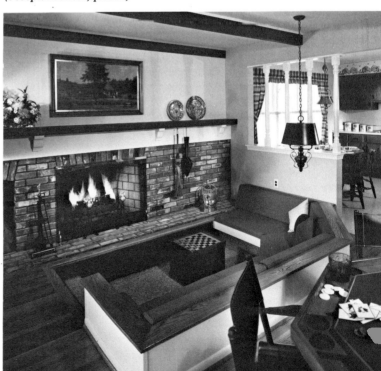

always be done. What we must do instead is create an area (square, rectangular, half circle, circle, or L-shaped) of comfort and repose. To achieve this, for example, two sofas can face each other over a low coffee table in front of the fire with two comfortable lounge chairs opposite the fireplace.

Do not forget to leave room for the business of fire tending, but not enough to allow traffic back and forth between the fireplace and furniture grouping.

The size of the furniture pieces and the grouping as a whole must be in proportion with the large mass of the fireplace. Two small arm chairs, for instance, would be lost in front of a massive fieldstone fireplace, but could be used with a smaller one.

35

3. For appearances sake!

Now that you and your family have planned the fireplace location to meet your needs, it is time to consider the outside appearance of the fireplace front and hearth. You have decided how much you wish to emphasize the fireplace in your room, whether you wish your fireplace to dominate, or to blend in smoothly with the general decor of the room.

If your desire is the fireplace of quiet importance, that adds to the warmth and graciousness of a room without great emphasis, there are many ways of achieving this result. One method of fitting a fireplace modestly into a wall so that it is an important feature, but not the dominant one, is to pair it off with another center of attraction. A fireplace set into a storage and bookcase wall, its design being an integral part of the wall's overall design, can be very restful and pleasing. This is a particularly good combination as it puts the books close by the comfortable seating arranged facing the hearth for cozy fireside reading. Another way to blend a fireplace in with the room is to surround it with attractive wood paneling, which covers the entire wall. Setting the fireplace in the window wall is yet another interesting combination which results in a concentration of interest. An added bonus to concentrating the main focus of interest into one spot is that one seating arrangement enjoys both the view and the fire at the same time.

Facing Materials

The materials used on the fireplace front will greatly influence the impact of the fireplace upon the room. The facing may be covered with the same wood-paneling that is used on the other walls of the room, or with a brick of soft tones that blends with the warm color of the wood-paneling. For a dominating fireplace, a rough fieldstone facing or a shining copper hood holds the eye.

Fireplace in window wall results in a combination of interest. (California Redwood Association)

Dramatic country club fireplace. Hearth and side walls are of stabilized adobe brick and the design is of glazed and fired adobe. (Tidyman Studios, photo.)

36

Bookcases paired with fireplace as center of attraction.
(Joseph Molitor, photo.)

Modest fireplace with raised hearth blends well with
Flame Gum paneling. (Georgia-Pacific)

Masonry Designs

REMOVABLE KINDLING TRAY

An effective use of brick as a facing, with a relatively simple fireplace.

Excellent use of brick in large projecting fireplace and walls of living room. (Herrlin Studio, photo.)

ELEVATION   SECTION
MODERN CONSTRUCTION APPLIED TO EARLY AMERICAN MANTEL - FACE FLUSH

Ceramic tile raised hearth with tile wall and hood. (U.S. Ceramic Tile Council)

Slate hearth cantilevered over wood storage and duplicate lower hearth. (Joseph Molitor, photo.)

The actual construction of the fireplace makes a difference, too. A fireplace built into a masonry wall with no projections, will blend right into the wall itself. If you add a contrasting cantilevered hearth and a large black metal hood, the result is eye-stopping. The ultimate example of a dramatic fireplace is a free-standing one, open on all sides with seating arranged around it.

In general, we may say that brick is not only the most popular, but also the most versatile masonry material, suitable for any style interior. The type of brick and the way it is laid, along with the overall design of the fireplace, determine whether the fireplace will be traditional or modern, formal or informal.

Clay bricks and fire seem to complement each other very well. The two types of bricks most often used are common and face brick. Common brick is rough and porous, used on inner surfaces that do not show, but sometimes used in facings for an informal effect and low cost. Face brick is a hard surfaced type used for fireplace facings and exteriors, where a more formal appearance is desired. Used bricks are another possibility; with their weathered charm they are most suitable for Early American fireplaces and other informal interiors. Roman brick, with its long shape, produces strong horizontal lines and is particularly effective in modern settings.

There are many other masonry materials to choose from such as field stone, ledge rock, sandstone, Indiana limestone, adobe, tile, marble, and attractive rocks found in a nearby riverbed or rock pile on your lot. The choice depends on your own preference, on the overall architecture of the house, or on the textures and colors needed in one particular room.

Wood paneling is another pleasing and popular material for the fireplace facing. A wood paneled wall adds warmth and textural interest to a room. The colors and textures of wood and masonry complement each other and are good in combination.

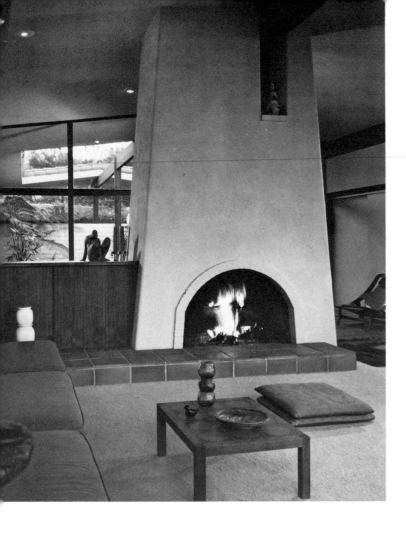

This imaginative fireplace screens living room from entrance foyer of house. (Buff & Hensman, Architects; Julius Shulman, photo.)

The wood wall may be in the style of formal Colonial paneling or may be rough barn-siding surrounding a large Early American hearth. A den seems to call for masculine pine-paneled walls, whereas redwood is particularly suitable for modern interiors, where it adds warmth to the sleek design.

There is a set of safety standards for fireplace facing which concerns the use of any combustible material such as wood trim or paneling. There should be 3-1/2″ minimum clearance on all sides of the fireplace opening. If the wood projects more than 1-1/2″ at the top of the opening, then the minimum clearance should be 12 inches at that point. Check your local code about this, as requirements differ across the country.

Hearth

The fireplace hearth is, basically, a rectangle of masonry or other fireproof material laid in front of the fireplace opening to protect the floor from sparks and the heat of the fire. The materials used and the design of the hearth, however, play an important part in the appearance of your fireplace.

The hearth may be flush with the floor, raised, or cantilevered. The floor level hearth can be spread over more of an area than simply that required for safety. It may extend out to enclose the whole seating area or may even be recessed below floor level to dramatize the fireplace and its surrounding space. The raised hearth serves to bring the fireplace up to an intimate height and is especially good for bedrooms, dining rooms and dens. The space under the raised hearth may be filled in with masonry or could provide convenient wood storage. If the raised hearth is long enough, cushions may be placed on it for informal seating.

The cantilevered hearth is an excellent way to dramatize the fireplace and may project out quite far and extend the whole length of the fireplace wall for a really striking design. The use of a contrasting material for the hearth adds to the dramatic effect of the strong horizontal line.

The front fireplace hearth should extend 8 inches on each side of the fireplace opening and 16 inches out in front for minimum safety requirements. Again, you should check with your local codes on this.

Mantels

The mantel of the fireplace was one of the working parts when the fireplace was depended upon to cook the family's meals. It served as a warming shelf and could hold pots and seasonings. Later on, when the fireplace moved from the kitchen into the living room, the mantel was used primarily for decorative purposes. The style of the mantel was in keeping with the architectural style of the house and the mantelpiece became a display shelf for treasured family heirlooms.

Some contemporary designers have omitted the mantel entirely, preferring instead to keep only the essential

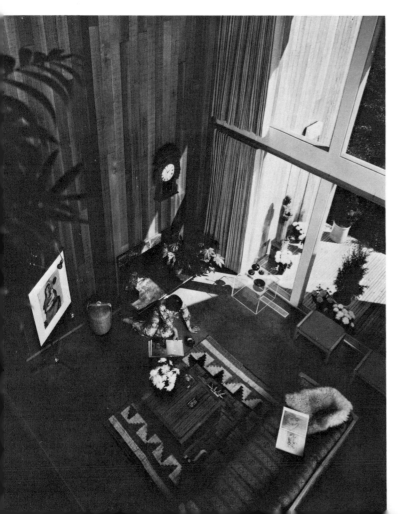

A striking interior, combining fireplace, window and mellow wood walls. (Western Wood Products)

A group of mill-built mantels from various periods.
(Endeavour Periods, Inc.)

features of the fireplace. Sometimes, however, the mantel is used as a device to tie in the fireplace with the architectural elements of the room.

Mantels are usually made of wood and they can be carpenter-made on the job or purchased ready-made from millwork houses.

There are many classical styles of wood mantel to choose from. You may select from the elaborate curved carving of a French or Victorian mantel piece to the classic refinement of detail of an Adam mantel, to the simple proportions of an Early American mantel. A heavy slab of wood set in a rough fieldstone fireplace may be suitable for a vacation home.

The design of the mantel should be planned carefully so that it is in keeping with the overall design of the hearth as it is a very effective decorative element. The wooden mantel may be painted to match the wall covering or the natural wood of the mantel may be finished to match the wood paneling in the room. In remodeling a room, a new mantel can be most effective and could help to update the fireplace or to change the feeling of the old fireplace entirely. The same safety restrictions mentioned earlier apply again here to the mantel.

Hoods

The fireplace hood can be the most striking feature of the hearth. The hood, of course, is not only decorative, but can increase the effectiveness of the fireplace by radiating heat when it is warmed up.

Fireplace hoods may be made of metal, plaster, or even masonry. The metals most often used are copper (polished, natural warm reddish tone, or oxidized green), aluminum and stainless steel, or steelplate painted charcoal black. The metal in the hood may be textured for added interest by hammering, sandblasting, etching, or polishing. Plaster hoods are made over a metal frame that covers the flue.

The shape of the hood adds to the feeling of warmth and interest which a fireplace brings to a room. There are

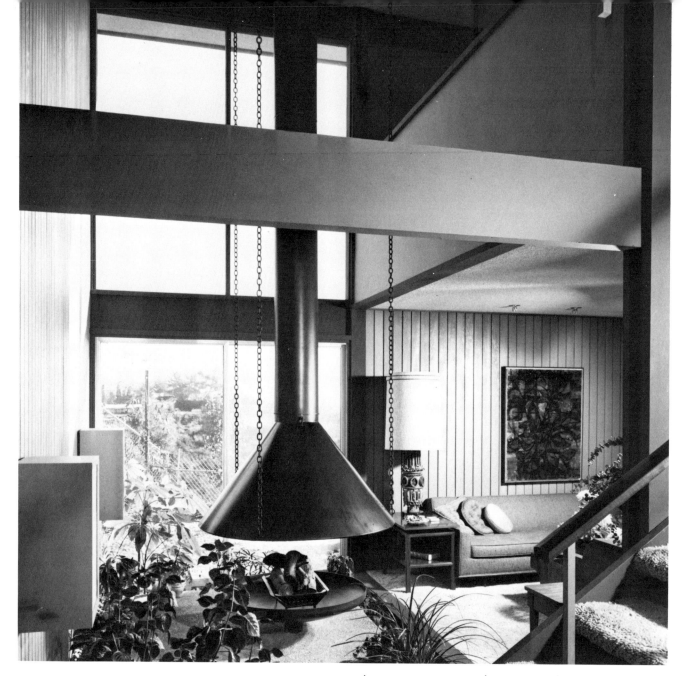

A two story space, opening to mezzanine bedroom area, utilizes hanging hood over aggregate floored hearth. (Buff & Hensman, Architects; Julius Shulman, photo.)

some traditional shapes for fireplace hoods or they may be freely designed to suit your individual needs. They may project from a fireplace wall or hang over a free-standing hearth.

Fireplace Furnishings and Accessories

The selection of furnishings and accessories for the fireplace deserves some time and thought. You may select them for purely utilitarian reasons or for ornamentation, hopefully a happy combination of both. Problems of size, proportion, and general appropriateness will have to be considered. Whatever is decided is likely to affect your

pleasure in using your fireplace and is fairly permanent in nature besides. Remind yourself, when making your selections, that the important thing is the fire itself and that you are trying to enhance the looks of the fireplace, not overpower it.

To carry and hold fuel, a coal hod or wood carrier, or both, will be needed. To support the burning fuel, fire basket, andirons, and log rest are the choices. To start the fire, perhaps a fire lighter (Chapter 10, Tending the Fire), will be needed. Tongs, log fork, and shovel feed the fire. A poker stirs it and a bellows may be useful in stimulating the flame.

Poker, tongs, log fork, brush and shovel are usually

Complete set of fireplace accessories includes swing out grill, tool set, canvas log carrier with cradle, log tongs, broom, bellows and long fireplace matches. (Seymour Mfg. Co.) (opposite below)

Pine paneled wall with book cases has mantel of same material. (opposite above)

Brass Woodbasket

Brass Coal Hod

Fireplace bellows. Brass, Naugahyde and walnut. (Seymour)

purchased in matched sets with a support of matching design or hung and a bracket fastened to the masonry. For a useful fireplace, select carefully for its utility as well as attractiveness. Many are made for appearances only and are not of adequate size or weight, or the handles may not have a good grip. There are many different designs available to match the style or design of your fireplace, available in brass, steel, and black finishes.

The choice of the fire basket or grate involves the question of size. A small basket in the middle of a large hearth presents a faulty appearance and also sacrifices warmth, since the flame does not reach and heat the surrounding brickwork enough to give back radiant heat. There are several designs available in fire baskets, making it possible to suit your fireplace. Some of the designs are adaptable to either coal or wood.

Where wood is the dominant fuel, and especially in larger fireplaces, a pair of heavy log rests afford the proper support. The heaviest log that is likely to be put in a fireplace will not warp these supports if they are good and sturdy.

Andirons are made in an infinite variety of shapes and sizes. The andiron represents a tradition that goes back to the earliest days of domestic fires, and originally was equipped with hooks and projections for the support of a spit or rod, from which other utensils were suspended. Modern use of the andirons are mostly for ornamentation. When choosing andirons select for suitable design and proper size. Most log rests, grates and fire baskets are designed so that the shank of an andiron will rest beneath, preserving the ornamental value of the andiron post even when other devices are bearing the fire load.

Firescreens

The basic types of firescreens include folding doors of tempered glass; standing screens that require no installation; and attached screens, mounted either outside or flush with the opening. Decide how you want your fireplace to look when it isn't being used—then you can be sure it will give you enjoyment when it is in use.

An oversize screen can make the fireplace seem much larger than it is and this may be desirable for the overall balance between the fireplace and the room. In addition to black and brass, other colors are available in screens and may be used to complement the scheme. Screens should be used to add to the appearance of a fireplace so it would be a mistake to use an ornate screen on a fireplace that is well designed and harmonizes with the room. Conversely, a screen may be used to conceal or modify a poorly designed fireplace.

The need for some type of screen stems from the danger of flying sparks. When fuel is used which tends to snap, such as cannel coal or some kinds of resinous woods, or when small children are playing in front of the fire, the screen should be used continuously. Also, for obvious reasons, the fireplace should always be screened if it is left to burn itself out when the family retires.

44

Log grate with open ends works well with all fireplaces.

Antique brass woodbasket, fireset and mesh firescreen. (Fred Meyer of California)

This type of firebasket is available in sizes to fit any fireplace, with splayed, square or open ends. Use with coal or wood.

4. an OUTLINE OF FIREPLACE HISTORY

Man's command of fire is one of the oldest and most important factors in his slow rise to civilization. Various peoples have their myths about the origin of this important blessing. Greek mythology gives credit to the titan Prometheus. A titan was supposed to be a creature midway between a god and a man.

Prometheus, says the story, stole fire from Zeus, the great god of the Greeks, and brought it down to man, thus miraculously saving mankind from the destruction which Zeus had planned.

There is a symbolical meaning to the myth, since Prometheus, in the Greek tongue, means forethought—not a bad adjunct in any project involving fire.

Wide Choice of Types

In the realm of the fireplace, nothing is new and nothing old. The earliest known types of fireplaces are among the novelties of today. The latest innovations have a record of centuries behind them.

The earliest indoor use of fire seems, everywhere, to have meant a hearth in the central open space of a dwelling. Such hearths existed in Britain before the coming of the Romans. They are found today in the island habitations of the Hebrides and among the crofters of Scotland,

with roof openings for the escape of smoke. Central hearths are not uncommon today among sophisticated seekers of novelty. A large one was erected in the center of a Chicago hotel lobby not long ago. However, these modern adaptations are fitted with inverted funnels to carry off the smoke—not mere holes in the roof.

Other Modern Antiquities

When the Romans encountered early Britain's rainy and forbidding chill, they brought braziers, fire pans on legs, not unlike a certain present-day type of lawn barbecue. The Romans also practiced what some innovators now call radiant heating, by piping flame and smoke through passages in walls and floors.

The heat circulating fireplace was invented in France about the year 1600, or a little later, and many times since. So instead of a sharply defined sequence of fireplace periods, we have a variety of forms that have existed in parallel over most of the eras of our study. The owner or designer of today's fireplace has great freedom in choosing forms, sizes and positions, but it is unlikely that he will create a wholly new type. On the other hand, no form that he can choose will be censured as outmoded.

Steer's head andirons and log rest of wrought iron.

Early smoke louvers.

46

Central Hearth Fireplace

The central hearth prevailed from earliest times until the sixteenth century, when the wall fireplace, first recorded in the tenth century, gained preference and became the prevailing type.

Central fires gave the occupants of the room all the benefit of direct radiation. The smoke eddying around the rafters and escaping through a roof opening must have deposited much soot and ash. But the offence may have been less than we imagine, for the fuel was wood, not the soot-breeding coal used in some fireplaces today. Yet Chaucer describes the apparel of the nun in his Canterbury Tales as being "full sooty."

Three incidental factors are worth mentioning. The hearth was often raised above the floor level, so there is nothing new about the "modern" elevation of the hearth. Smoke louvers, hollow, ventilated structures, surmounted the smoke opening and protected the interior against rain.

Early Andirons

The third feature to be noted is that the andiron was not an ornamental device as it often is today. When cooking was part of the function of the central fire, it was necessary to have a support for the spits on which meat was suspended over the fire. Andirons, with prongs and notches, supported the ends of the spit. They also supported heavier crossbars on which pots were hung. To steady the two andirons, a crossbrace often joined them, being welded to each a few inches above hearth level. This cross member also supported sticks of firewood, slanted against it.

Fireplaces Move to the Wall

When Norman barons commenced to build castles of more than one story, there was need for a means of heating upper and lower rooms separately, the central fire with roof outlet being no longer a possible resource. From this came the wall fireplace.

Fireplaces at the wall did not immediately mean chimneys, nor recesses in the wall. Most often, the fire was built on a hearth projecting forward from the masonry wall. Over the fire was a hood of metal or masonry, and back of the hood, at its upper extremity, was a hole extending slantwise through the wall that carried off the smoke.

Early hooded fireplaces generally lacked any side structure. Without jamb support, the hood was kept in place by a corbell or bracket anchored in the wall masonry. If the hood itself was of masonry construction, there was need of a lintel, which might be a heavy oak beam. Sometimes the side support also consisted of two wooden members, cantilevered through the thickness of the wall. Some old prints indicate hoods of semicircular section, but more often rectangular.

Partial recessing of the hearth followed, as well as the

Two early chimney tops, when utility alone was not enough.

Hooded Corner Fireplace, common to Sweden.

A side-wall fireplace in a foot-warming act.

After Scandinavian style, in tile and sculptured plaster with pine paneling.

Early Persian design. Extreme enclosure would ensure smoke control but would limit heating value.

Early Brittany, from a print. Note bed nook nearby.

development of chimneys that carried the smoke above roof level. In the Gothic, or Tudor, period we find great elaboration of the chimney, as shown in the illustration.

Separation of Purposes

In the castles and mansions of aristocrats, it was feasible to have separate fireplaces in various rooms, primarily for warmth, while the kitchen fireplace was a separate development, primarily devoted to the preparation of food. A number of cooks, scullions and spit boys might find employment there.

In cottages and farmhouses, a single fireplace served both for warmth and for cookery. The later type usually had both a fire chamber and an enclosed oven, built into the masonry at one side. Occasionally there would be ovens on both sides. In any case there would be cranes, trivets, pots, pans, spits, etc.

Such fireplaces served colonial homes for generations, although prosperous folks might also have parlor fireplaces. Sometimes the kitchen type of fireplace would be very wide, so that the fire, occupying the central portion, left room for stools or benches in the "ingle nook." Genrally it was the privilege of the elderly to sit in the chimney corner.

Such fireplaces continued in practical service for many years and may, in out of the way places, be in use today.

The pioneer cooking fireplace, in a somewhat contracted and refined form, is the most frequently copied of any of the distinctly earlier types. And this is not mere antiquarian affectation. All over America we find casual meals being cooked much as our ancestors prepared them.

In Continental Lands

In Germany there was an early trend toward enclosing the fire in brick or tile structures, often with iron doors that could be opened. Thus came the Nuremberg stove.

The Scandinavian countries developed a type of corner fireplace of distinctive characteristics. While occupying a corner position, such a fireplace is often quite free from the wall, so that a person can walk around behind it. The hearth is raised and the massive masonry hood is supported by heavy timber lintels. At the forward corner, there is a column support, often a disused gun barrel. The hood is credited with retaining much heat.

Our interest in French fireplaces is chiefly grounded in the wealth of experimental activity in the seventeenth and eighteenth centuries, directed toward making the fireplace a more efficient heating unit. However, French mansions and chateaux participated in the ornamental phases of fireplace development, a phase of history which cannot be overlooked.

Baronial Types of Fireplaces

Throughout the middle ages and well into the renaissance, architects devoted their most earnest efforts to creating fireplace structures which should glorify as well as warm the noble residents of the mansions thus distinguished.

Every resource of architectural design, of painting, sculpture and heraldry were enlisted in this type of enterprise.

Surviving examples of such fireplaces have little significance for us today, save in the matter of emphasis. They did firmly distinguish the fireplace as the focal emblem of family cohesion and home loyalty—a principle which, we trust, will never be lost to sight.

Steps in Development

Fireplaces have approached their present shape or shapes by passing through the following phases. (1) The central hearth with roof outlet. (2) Hooded fireplaces with wall outlet. (3) Development of the chimney. (4) Decrease of size as coal became the prevailing fuel. (5) Reflector-like back and narrowed throat. (6) Development of the throat damper.

These steps bring us to the best current practice in the building of masonry fireplaces. But they do not, by any means, sum up all the efforts made to improve the open fire as a source of available warmth. Increasing skill in casting of iron offered inventors an inspiration to experiment in more involved shapes for the fireplace interior. Hence there came, in the seventeenth and eighteenth centuries, a flow of new suggestions in fireplace practice.

Inventions Re-invented

Similar ideas were embodied again and again in the conceptions of these pioneers. Three principal objects stand out—(1) Introduction of the downdraft principle, by which smoke was drawn down behind a false back or core before reaching the flue, with the presumable purpose of consuming smoke. (2) Passing air over heated surfaces and discharging it into the room, supplementing direct radiation with circulated warm air. (3) Introduction of air from outside the building to furnish oxygen for combustion and draft for discharge of the products of combustion.

Heat-circulation Pioneers

Of these three innovations, the only one that has survived has been the second one mentioned. So far as we know, the first man to propose increasing the heat delivery of a fireplace by circulating heat was Louis Savot, a court physician interested in the public health problems of France. He built a fireplace in the Louvre in the early decades of the seventeenth century. He died in 1640, 66 years before Franklin was born, which interests Americans because many have the impression that the heat circulating fireplace was first exemplified in Franklin's Pennsylvania Fireplace.

All of the many early fireplaces of this type were doomed to brief success, if any. The fact was that cast iron was a poor medium from which to fabricate the air cham-

Dutch design—these were usually decorated with tiles, made at Delft.

Detail of tile design in similar fireplace. (Amsterdam Corp.)

An Italian Renaissance fireplace

From the ruins of an Italian palace, this fireplace was transported to this country and reassembled.

bers and ducts necessary in a fireplace of this type. Exposed to variable temperatures of open flame, it tended to crack or warp, letting smoke into the warm-air passage.

It was not until the development of the welding of metal plate that the principle of heat circulation became practical. Meantime a century had elapsed in which the idea had lain dormant. There are at least a half dozen brands of welded fireplace units made in the United States today.

Other Innovators

English fireplace chronicles speak of a fireplace contrived for Prince Rupert, a cousin of King Charles II, by a mason named Bingham, that employed the downdraft principle, the smoke being drawn downward behind a false back, about half the distance to hearth level, before ascending to the flue. In starting the fire, a valve plate was provided that permitted direct ascent, the valve plate being closed when the fire was well started.

Sir John Winter is credited with being the first to introduce outdoor air as a source of draft, but the honor of first combining this ventilating feature with the principle of circulation seems to belong to a Frenchman named Gauger, who also recognized the importance of shaping the sides and back to afford the effect of a reflector. His work was publicized in 1713 in England by Desaguliers, who

Copied from a design by Violet Le Duc, no record of how well it burned.

Savot design: air entered below raised hearth, returned to room through openings below mantel shelf.

first applied the term "ventilation." His efforts as a promoter met little success.

American Innovators

Benjamin Franklin included among his varied accomplishments a discriminating knowledge of fireplace principles, and creative ability that gave rise to the so called Pennsylvania Fireplace, as well as the celebrated Franklin Stove, an enclosed heating device.

A long letter written by Franklin, while on shipboard, returning to America, is one of the clearest expositions of fireplace principles and practice ever penned. It was written to Jan Ingenhousz, a Dutch scientist and engineer living in London.

The man who has done the most, perhaps, to shape the trend of modern fireplace practice, however, was a New Englander, born at Woburn, Massachusetts, named Benjamin Thompson. But he left America early in life and never returned. In the course of a distinguished European career, he was honored with the title of Count Rumford. Fireplaces based on principles that he expounded are known as Rumford fireplaces.

Thompson's public career was enacted in Munich, where he filled several cabinet posts and was virtual ruler of Bavaria, being given the title of Count of the Holy Roman Empire. He chose to be called Count Rumford, since Rumford, N.H., had been his most recent American home.

Deeply interested in science, he returned to London after a decade and it was here that his work on fireplaces was chiefly carried out. Where other innovators had resorted much to use of iron, he relied on brick, except in the fire basket. He made fireplaces smaller and shallower than the prevailing types, with narrow back and wide flaring sides. Smoke escaped through a narrow throat placed well forward by slope of the back wall and with a rather high smoke shelf. At the height of his London experience, he mentions having some 500 smoky chimneys under his care. His fireplace designs are prized for their simplicity, fuel economy and high heat delivery.

The Pennsylvania Fireplace

Franklin described his Pennsylvania Fireplace in a pamphlet offered for sale in 1844. It embodies all three of the objects referred to in listing the basic aspects of the "iron age" of fireplaces—ventilation, down-draft, and heat circulation.

Fire was built in the forward chamber of the metal unit. Heat and smoke passed over the top of a central hot-air chamber, being drawn down to a level below the level of the hearth and then discharged upward behind a false fireback of brick. The false back was connected with the fireplace breast by a sloping slab of stone or slate. Air drawn from outdoors fed the central hot-air chamber, where it was warmed and discharged through openings at the sides.

(above)
Early American fireplace complex

Early American; comes very close to Count Rumford standards. Note the oven at the right side.

Another early design of warm-air fireplace, shows the many joints that were its weakness.

SECOND FLOOR FIREPLACES

WOOD BEAMS

SEPARATE OVEN

51

Franklin describes the advantages of heat circulation: even heat throughout the room, people warm on both sides, whether they sit near the fire or near a window. Evidence is lacking as to the number of Pennsylvania Fireplaces built in America, but we know there were some. Governor Thomas of Pennsylvania offered him a patent, but he declined as—"glad to serve others by any invention of ours"—since he had profited by the inventions of others.

Esthetic Developments

The recorded history of fireplaces in the seventeenth and eighteenth centuries is chiefly the story of grand installations in the mansions of aristocrats. Consequently much more is told us about period styles and overmantel decorations than about the working features of the fireplaces.

Such noted architects as Inigo Jones and Christopher Wren established standards of dignity and importance in styling which inspired scores of successors. The most talented artists, wood carvers and cabinet makers took pride in glorifying the great halls of the English nobility with eye-compelling treatments of this focal feature.

Few of these treatments are such as we would wish to imitate today, except in watered-down form. They mark an era, however, when the open fire was still the main resource for heating.

Victorian Andirons—a blend of Chinese and rococo styles, were used in the White House, according to family records, during the administration of President Taylor. They are now in the Treaty Room. (Copyright by White House Historical Association. Photograph by National Geographic Society.)

The Family Dining Room on the State Floor of the White House is furnished with American pieces of the Federal Period. A gilt convex mirror crowned with an eagle hangs above the white-and-green-marble mantelpiece. (Copyright by White House Historical Association. Photograph by National Geographic Society.)

The Empire Marble Mantelpiece in the White House Green Room is one of a pair ordered by James Monroe after the fire of 1814. Note the cast iron firebox. The fire tools and andirons are American; the latter were made by Richard Wittingham in New York. (Copyright by White House Historical Assocation. Photograph by National Geographic Society.)

(opposite)
The Green Room—a Federal Parlor in the White House. Empire Marble mantelpiece. Above the fireplace hangs the famous portrait of Benjamin Franklin by David Martin. (Copyright by White House Historical Association. Photograph by National Geographic Society.)

52

Franklin Stove in a prepared recess. More commonly it was set away from the wall.

(right, above)
The Dining Room fireplace in Jefferson's Monticello home, showing the Wedgewood plaques in the mantel and the dumb waiter which connected with the wine room below. (Thomas Jefferson Memorial Foundation)

Mantels

Early endeavour by original craftsmen to introduce definitely authentic architectural design to mantels occurred as early as 1600 A.D.

The Elizabethan Period ushered in massive mantels of hand-hewn and carved stone which were focal points of the great castle halls. This style, with soaring chimney piece, continued into the Stuart period, and magnificent examples are treasured in Scotland, England and Ireland today.

English Georgian mantels of the 1700's were the first wooden mantels with architectural authenticity. Early Georgian designs were tall, proportioned for the high ceilings of great houses, and often carried elaborate carvings. They are distinguished by stately design of the overhanging mantel body, and moulded step corner on the frieze.

French Louis mantels, as was the furniture of the Louis', were elegantly decorative. They introduced the classic French curve. A shell motif accentuated by fine scroll work and stately contoured pillars further emphasized the natural beauty of curving lines. The mantel shelf, similarly contoured, repeated the graceful design.

The Regency period, beginning around 1810, shows even further design refinement, with the influence of French Louis styling easily apparent.

An early "family room" with cooking fireplace.

The Victorian period, extending from 1832 to 1900, featured relatively simple mantel designs. Raised paneling effects with heavy center ornamental detail, and semicircular firebox openings, were the general rule. In the early years, cast iron Victorian mantels were used extensively throughout the British Isles.

Adam Mantels, designed by Scottish architect Robert Adam in collaboration with his talented brothers, James and William, are among the most classically beautiful, and were seen in fine homes of the Victorian period. Highly decorative, they often showed a strong Greek influence with the use of the fret, lamp and scroll motifs. Marble inlay panels were features of the most highly refined designs, and carved ribbons, bows and swags were adopted.

Spanish Architecture adapted and blended various styles and periods. The influence of Early English Gothic and Italian church periods is expressed clearly in many Spanish mantel designs.

Italian Mantels showed the individual artisan's characteristic expression of favored romantic baroque styling.

American Colonial designs were primarily adaptations of old world periods. Some were simple stone with heavy wood slab mantel shelf supported by wood or stone corners. Later, in many of the fine homes, copies of the Grecian fluted pillar, the ribbon and shell, and other more sophisticated design details were executed by early American cabinet makers.

From: *The Endeavour Periods, Inc.*

The Auxiliary Role

While it is probable that better and more efficient fireplaces are being built today than at any time past, they have ceased to be the main reliance for heating. Most residences in cooler climates have provision for central heating. They have gas or electric cooking facilities.

Highly appreciated in Spring and Fall or other chilly periods when central plants are not in use, indispensable in extreme cold or when public utilities fail, delightful in its power to charm at any time, the fireplace remains largely an auxiliary in the practical domain of home economy.

Fireplaces with Ovens

Some form of oven for baking and roasting has existed from time beyond record. Often it had an outdoor location. In other cases, it occupied a shed, apart from the residence. Such free-standing ovens generally betokened use as a utility for a neighborhood such as prevailed in colonial Virginia. Where the housewife wrestled with food preparation alone, it has been logical to make the oven a part of

English fireplace at time of Queen Victoria. Curtain at top of fireplace indicates an effort to correct a smoking tendency.

Another fireplace from early American days. (Firelands Museum, Norwalk, Ohio)

A close replica of an early large fireplace with wood lintel.
This shows many of the cooking facilities depended on in
those days.

Early American taproom fireplace

Another Franklin fireplace inserted in conventional opening. (Thomas Paine Cottage, New Rochelle, N.Y.)

Woodwork was brought from an old castle in England, wooden pegs used for fastening. Date 1590 appears below coat of arms.

the fireplace. In England and in New England the term kitchen oven was used to distinguish such ovens from larger outdoor ovens or those occupying a detached shed.

Operation consisted of introducing hot coals into the oven and leaving them there until the masonry was thoroughly heated. Coals were then raked out and bread dough or other substance to be baked was introduced and the interior tightly closed until baking was complete. Similarly the oven accomplished slow roasting of meats, as an alternative to the more rapid grilling or spit roasting before an open flame.

The Dutch Oven Today

Enthusiasm for fireplace cooking, outdoor and indoor, has restored the Dutch Oven to favor as a feature of combination outdoor fireplaces and of indoor barbecues as well as those fireplaces more definitely classed as reproductions of Early American types. It should be noted, however, that the term Dutch Oven has been applied in certain times and, in places, to quite different metal contrivances.

The present day modification of this historic feature is the introduction of a compact fire chamber under the oven proper, where a charcoal fire can be maintained. This fits the oven for the cooking that is not suitable to the Range Unit, which is usually the dominant feature of combination fireplaces.

Modified Operation

Cooking or baking can be much more rapid with an active charcoal fire below the oven. This fire can be fed without disturbing the oven. An adequate vent is highly important. It may communicate with the main flue, or with an independent flue.

Metal parts necessary for a modern Dutch Oven include the ornamental Dutch Oven Door, a smaller ash door and necessary grates for the support of the fire and the viands being cooked. By locating the level of the charcoal grate above the floor of the fire chamber, ashes may be conveniently raked out.

Importance of History

For as long as mankind continues to use and enjoy the fireplace, its rich historical background will have significance. Today's home dweller, as he sits before his fireplace, establishes his most tangible link with the great ages of the past.

Present fireplace forms have grown out of forms with centuries of tradition behind them. Their stabilizing effect on an era prone to restless innovation accounts in large measure for the increasing vogue of this long established domestic institution.

5. CONVENTIONAL FIREPLACES

The conventional masonry fireplace has become the standard in America—by being suitable to our needs; adaptable to our fuels of wood or coal; moderate in cost, or elaborately expensive to suit the variable needs or desires; enjoyable in home, cottage, camp, club, office or mansion; as a main source of heat and comfort or, in buildings with central heat, as a supplemental or emergency heat source, and, in all cases providing the nostalgic, heart-warming pleasures of a blazing log fire.

Planning the location, size, and general character of your fireplace is a subject worthy of careful study by architects, builders, homeowners, and masons. Factors of location, interior planning and design are covered in Chapter 2.

Handicap of Too Large a Fireplace. Top—fireplace too large for fire. Radiates less heat than where flame fits the fireplace smoothly—as bottom.

The Question of Size

Home planners often need to be warned against the sentimental desire for "a great big fireplace." They forget that a great big fire would probably drive them out of the room. They need to be told that a small fire in a big fireplace is not efficient heating.

As mentioned earlier, a fireplace thirty inches wide, well filled with flame, will provide more heat than the same fire built in a larger fireplace.

Heat radiated from a fireplace comes, to a large extent, from the heated brickwork that surrounds the flame. The closer the brickwork to the flame, the more it is heated. In the case of the thirty-inch fireplace in the diagram above, the back and sides are both heated. In the forty-eight-inch fireplace, only a portion of the back masonry is heated. More heat undoubtedly goes up the chimney.

The larger fireplace requires a larger flue. In case of the forty-eight-inch opening, the flue lining would have to be the sixteen-inch-by-sixteen-inch size, while the smaller, thirty-inch fireplace would be adequately served by a twelve-inch-by-twelve-inch flue. To maintain a steady draft, the larger flue would need 50 per cent more air from some source. With a moderate-size fire, it probably would not get such a volume of air. The up-draft would tend to be sluggish and, if ventilation were restricted, there would be a tendency to downdraft. And, presuming that a good draft were established in the larger flue, there would plainly be more cold air to heat.

So, plan no larger fire than your room requires, and plan the fireplace to fit the fire snugly if you want maximum warmth.

Plans

If carefully tested plans such as those shown in this book are used, or the fireplace is built in accord with the tables and technical standards provided, the operation should be completely satisfactory. Where trouble is encountered it will be found to be caused by some environmental condition or the violation of the basic rules found herein.

Details—Back-to-back fireplace installation.
(Garlinghouse Plan Service, Topeka, Kansas)

LIVING ROOM ELEVATION

UPPER LEVEL PLAN

LOWER LEVEL PLAN

SECTION X-X

SECTION Y-Y

Chimney Cap
Available precast for some standard flue sizes or cast in place. Note that the liner projects through the cap several inches.

Flue and Flue Lining
The area of the flue should equal one-twelfth to one-eighth the area of the opening of the fireplace (width times height). Lining is supported on masonry.

Smoke Chamber
Together with the smoke shelf, this area is important to a smoke free fire. Both sides slope to the flue and it is important that they slope identically, otherwise the fire will burn on one side of the firebox only.

The entire smoke chamber and smoke shelf is parged with fire clay mortar (refractory mortar) or type "S" mortar one-half inch thick.

Throat and Damper
These parts are usually one and the same. The damper is capable of being opened and closed gradually to control the draft and keep out cold air when the fireplace is not in use. The opening in square inches should be at least 90% of that required for the flue.

Firebox
This is the area that comes alive with dancing flames and gleaming embers. To do this the firebox must be correctly proportioned, sealed, vented, and well constructed.

Smoke Shelf
This is a horizontal shelf, usually concave and extending backward from the rear of the throat or damper to the rear flue wall. It directs cold air downdrafts which are present in the early stages of the fire, causing them to eddy and drift upward with the rising air currents.

Hearth
The inner hearth is that portion within the fire area and is usually built of fire brick but may be other types of hard brick, concrete, stone, tile or other non-combustible heat-resistant materials. The outer hearth is built of the same type materials and should extend a minimum of eight inches on each side of the fireplace opening and sixteen inches in front. (Note: These figures are twelve inches and eighteen inches in areas covered by the Uniform Building Code.)

Ashpit
This is the hollow space below the hearth into which ashes fall through the ash dump door located in the hearth. A metal door is provided in the ashpit for the occasional removal of ashes. In basementless homes, particularly those built on a concrete slab, it may not be feasible to provide an ashpit unless the hearth has been raised. In this case the ashpit door faces outside.

Foundation
Consult your local building code, since these codes differ according to existing soil and moisture conditions in individual areas. If total weight is needed to compute the depth and rise of the foundation required, figure brick at 130 lbs. and concrete at 150 lbs. per cubic foot. For cubic footage, figure the entire cross section volume including the open portion of the flue and firebox. The footing should extend at least below the depth of the greatest frost penetration.

As a general rule, footings should be of concrete at least twelve inches thick and should extend at least six inches on all sides of the foundation. Concrete should be poured on undisturbed soil.

Foundation walls should be a minimum of eight inches thick.

Materials

Brick, concrete block, stone and adobe may be used in fireplace construction. Hollow concrete block should only be used in the foundation and ashpit areas. Fire brick, soapstone, or other refractory material must be used to line the firebox, and fire brick or flue tile should be used for the inner course of the flue.

Steel fireplace lining, at least one-fourth inch thick, may be used instead of fire brick. Installation should be in accordance with manufacturers' recommendations.

Mortar. Setting fire brick and parging in smoke chamber—use fire clay mortar (refractory mortar). Masonry mortar should not be used for parging.

Flue lining—use fire clay mortar or type M or S. (Table) All other mortar shall be type S or N. Mortar should be used within two and a half hours of mixing. Calcium chloride may be added to accelerate setting and hardening in winter weather only in an amount not to

Cleanout door for ash pit. (Heatilator Fireplaces)

Ash dump, cast iron.

exceed one per cent by weight of the Portland Cement. It should be added in solution as part of mixing water.

Flue Lining should be clay tile manufactured in accordance with ASTM C-315-56. Thickness increases with size from a minimum of 5/8" to 1-5/8" for the twenty-four-inch-by-twenty-four-inch size.

Mortar Mix[1]

Mortar type	Portland cement or Portland blast furnace slag cement	Hydrated lime or lime putty[2]	Type II masonry cement	Aggregate[2]
M	1	¼	------------	3 to 3¾
	1	------------	1	4½ to 6
S	1	¼ to ½	------------	3¼ to 4½
	½	------------	1	3¼ to 4½
N	1	½ to 1	------------	4 to 6
	------------	------------	1	2¼ to 3

[1]Proportion by volume.
[2]Damp, loose condition.

Chain Control Damper

Rotary Control Damper

High formed damper incorporates throat construction. (Majestic)

Smoke dome for use in multiple opening fireplaces. (Majestic)

Standard Liners		Modular Liners		Round Liners	
Outside Dimensions	Area of Passage	Nominal Outside Dimensions	Area of Passage	Inside Diameter	Area of Passage
8½ × 8½	52.56	8 × 12	57	8	50.26
		8 × 16	74		
8½ × 13	80.50			10	78.54
		12 × 12	87		
8½ × 18	109.69	12 × 16	120	12	113.00
13 × 13	126.56	16 × 16	162	15	176.70
13 × 18	182.84	16 × 20	208		
18 × 18	248.06	20 × 20	262	18	254.40
		20 × 24	320	20	314.10
		24 × 24	385	22	380.13
				24	452.30

Three different methods of measurement are employed for the three types of flue lining: outside measurement for the old standard; "nominal" outside dimensions for the modular standard; and the inside diameter for the round linings. Whatever type of lining is used, the sectional areas provide a guide for the desired flue capacity, which should be based on a sectional area not less than one tenth or one eighth the flue area, depending on the chimney height.

Metal Parts should be of approved manufacture. Dampers must have the ability to close the throat effec-

tively and the opening should be adjustable by rotary face control, poker, or chain control. Damper should extend the width of the firebox and when open have an area equal to 90 per cent of the required flue area. High formed dampers are available which incorporate the throat construction and, because of their extra height and width, allow a shallower fireplace. Without the need to construct a throat of brick and mortar, labor costs are reduced. Consult manufacturers' literature.

Special dome dampers incorporating damper, smoke chamber, and lintel are available for multi-opening fireplaces. When used, the fireplace should be built in accordance with the manufacturer's literature covering the dome.

Dimensions

Finished Opening							Rough Masonry				
A	B	C	D	E	F	G	H	I	K		
Width	Height	Depth	Back	Throat	Width	Depth	Smoke Shelf Height	Smoke Chamber	Vertical Back	Standard Flue Lining	Modular Flue Lining
24	28	16	16	9	30	19	32	11	14	8½ × 8½	8 × 12
26	28	16	18	9	32	19	32	11	14	8½ × 8½	8 × 12
28	28	16	20	9	34	19	32	11	14	8½ × 13	12 × 12
30	30	16	22	9	36	19	34	11	15	8½ × 13	12 × 12
32	30	16	24	9	38	19	34	11	15	8½ × 13	12 × 12
34	30	16	26	9	40	19	34	11	15	8½ × 13	12 × 12
36	31	18	27	9	42	21	36	11	16	13 × 13	12 × 16
38	31	18	29	9	44	21	36	11	16	13 × 13	12 × 16
40	31	18	31	9	46	21	36	11	16	13 × 13	12 × 16
42	31	18	33	9	48	21	36	11	16	13 × 13	12 × 16
44	32	18	35	9	50	21	37	11	17	13 × 13	12 × 16
46	32	18	37	9	52	21	37	11	17	13 × 13	12 × 16
48	32	20	38	9	54	23	37	15½	17	13 × 18	16 × 20
50	34	20	40	9	56	23	39	15½	18	13 × 18	16 × 20
52	34	20	42	9	58	23	39	15½	18	13 × 18	16 × 20
54	34	20	44	9	60	23	39	15½	18	13 × 18	16 × 20
56	36	20	46	9	62	23	41	15½	19	18 × 18	20 × 20
58	36	22	47	9	64	25	41	15½	19	18 × 18	20 × 20
60	36	22	49	9	66	25	41	15½	19	18 × 18	20 × 20

A—Two Faces Adjacent

w	d	h	flue
30	30	36	16 × 16
34	20	30	12 × 16
42	24	42	16 × 20

B—Two Faces Opposite

w	d	h	flue
30	24	42	16 × 20
34	28	30	16 × 16
38	28	36	16 × 20

C—Three Faces

w	d	h	flue
34	24	24	16 × 16
38	28	30	16 × 20
38	28	36	20 × 24

Flue areas for fireplaces having 2 or more openings (faces). (Federal Housing Administration)

Design

A great deal of the satisfaction to be gained from a conventional masonry fireplace will depend on adherence to proper proportioning of the opening, throat, flue, etc. Many of the recommended dimensions and proportions used in fireplacing vary from source to source and from building code to code. What we attempt to do here is to present a consensus. If these rules are followed, you should have a successful fireplace.

Dimensions
    Width—24″ to 84″ opening
    Height—2/3 to 3/4 of the width
    Depth—1/2 to 2/3 of the height
    Flue Area—FHA requirements are:

Area of the flue:
—one-tenth of the area of fireplace opening for chimneys fifteen feet in height or over.
—one-eighth of area of fireplace opening for chimneys under fifteen feet in height.
—Corner fireplaces or fireplaces open on two or more sides should be designed for each specific installation. The detail shown on this page may be used as a guide.
—Height of chimney is measured from fireplace throat to top.
—The above is for rectangular flues lined with flue lining or fire brick.
—At altitudes over 2000 feet the area of the flue and the height of the chimney should be increased 5 per cent for each 1000 feet of elevation. Check with local building official.

Multiple Opening Fireplaces

These fireplaces can be built so as to be useful and enjoyable and so as to contribute to the decor of the room or rooms on which they face, but they are not exempt from the general principles of construction that govern all successful fireplaces. As with regular wall type fireplaces, the size of openings should be in proportion to the size of the room. These fireplaces are of three types: corner, two- and three-way fireplaces.

    In determining the flue area, you must count the area of each open face. The drawing and table shows the areas recommended by the Federal Housing Administration. Dampers used are usually of a special type and fireplaces should be built in accordance with the damper manufacturer's instructions.

Corner Fireplaces

These fireplaces should have a sloping back wall like conventional fireplaces. The open end of this fireplace (around the corner from the principal face) can have a short wall, four inches to eight inches, to act as a baffle in the event of cross drafts. This is particularly desirable in the event the fireplace juts into the room like a peninsula.

FIREPLACE DETAILS

Multiple opening fireplace. (Not to scale) Note in plan and section B-B of corner fireplace how short baffle wall is corbeled to slope of firebrick. Baffle wall minimizes effect of cross drafts. (Garlinghouse Plan Service, Topeka, Kansas)

Corner fireplaces can be built without a supporting corner post by use of specially designed lintels to cantilever the brick work around the corner.

Two Way-Double Opening Fireplace

These are located in a chimney stack that serves as a partition. By building one fire you cheer and warm two rooms. Care should be taken that potential cross drafts such as a front and a rear door in line with the firebox do not spread smoke and ashes into one of the rooms.

Three-Way Fireplace

This fireplace can be a peninsula like the corner fireplace and part of a room dividing masonry mass, or it can project from a sidewall into the room. In effect, this fireplace would bring the fire into the center of the family circle. As in the corner fireplace, short walls are sometimes a safeguard against smoking.

Air Supply for Combustion

It takes air to run a fireplace—air for draft, oxygen for combustion. In homes of past generations this was some-times supplied overabundantly. The roaring logs drew drafts through every chink and cranny of window or door. Chairs with wings at the level of the face were provided to keep off drafts from the rear, while the face and shins toasted.

Until recent times there has been little difficulty in securing the moderate up-draft needed for the operation of the present-day fireplace. But newer techniques of weatherstripping and caulking and the use of special gaskets on casement windows have made many a modern interior tight as a drum. Furthermore, if a furnace or an incinerator is operating, the only source from which they can get needed combustion air is down the fireplace chimney. The down-draft that this creates prevents maintaining a fire on the hearth. Even if there is no other fire in the interior, perfect tightness can prevent the building of a satisfactory open fire.

The solution to all these problems is ventilated interiors. The slight opening of a basement window, if there is no other ventilating device, will generally provide the air needed for the fireplace, furnace, and incinerator. Another solution is to install a special ventilating brick between the outside and the ashpit. This will supply air through the ash dump for the fire.

PLAN OF
FIREBOX

SIDES SPLAYED 3" TO 5"
FOR EACH FOOT OF DEPTH,
OR AT ABOUT 15°

SMOKE
SHELF

ARROWS INDICATE
HEAT DEFLECTION
INTO THE ROOM

SECTION
THRU FIREBOX

Proper firebox angles maximize reflected heat to room.

THROAT TO BE
AS WIDE AS
FIREPLACE
WIDTH

Importance of throat design. Note how smoke shelf deflects down drafts, causing them to mix with hot gases and go back up the flue.

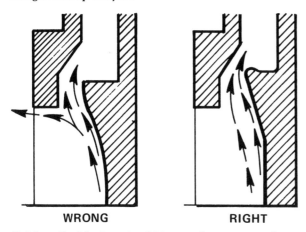

WRONG   RIGHT

Brick wall of firebox should be angular, not curved.

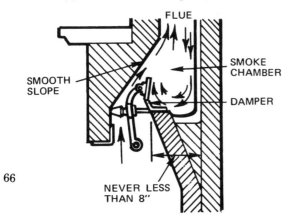

FLUE

SMOOTH
SLOPE

SMOKE
CHAMBER

DAMPER

NEVER LESS
THAN 8"

Shape of the Fireplace. For maximum heat radiation, the sides of the fireplace should be splayed three to five inches for each foot of depth or about 15 degrees. The back wall should not be built on a vertical curve as it may encourage smoke to enter the room. The wall should have a vertical portion (see table) and then slope forward to the throat. The ash dump should be located under the fire.

Where a cheerful fireplace without maximum heat is desired, the firebox may be rectangular in shape, as wide in the rear as in the front. Heat can be further minimized by a larger flue and damper.

Throat-Smoke Chamber. The throat of the fireplace should always be as wide as the firebox is wide and from four to five inches in depth. Modern dampers (drawing) are constructed to combine the damper and the throat which automatically insures this detail of construction.

The back edge of the damper should always rest on the forward edge of the smoke shelf. The joint between the damper and the bottom of the smoke shelf should be sealed with mortar so that flames can only reach the flue through the damper throat. Ends of the damper should be installed to permit expansion from heat.

A great deal of care should be taken to see that proper dimensions are maintained in the smoke chamber; that the front of the wall is not drawn in so abruptly as to interfere with the rising smoke, and that all surfaces are smooth and free from large projections.

Chimney

Each fireplace should have a separate flue.

Chimney should extend at least two feet above any part of a roof, ridge, or parapet wall within ten feet of the chimney. This should be three feet on flat roofs.

All fireplace chimneys should have flue lining except when chimney walls are at least eight inches nominal thickness.

Chimney connectors (smoke pipes) where used to connect metal fireplaces to masonry chimneys should have a maximum length of ten feet or 75 per cent of the vertical height of the chimney, whichever is the lesser. A thimble (metal or clay form in chimney to receive smoke pipe) should be used.

Unequal projection of two or more flues in the same chimney is a safeguard against smoke pouring out one flue and down the other.

Proximity of a tree or high building may interfere with the free flow of smoke. The remedy is often found in hooding as shown here.

Chimneys should be flashed and counter-flashed with corrosion resistant metal where they penetrate the roof. A cricket or saddle should be used on the high side of a sloping roof to shed the water around the chimney. (Basis—FHA 902-7 P. 163)

A chimney cap should be provided of concrete or other non-combustible material. Cap should be sloped from flue to outside edge with a minimum thickness of 2 inches. No masonry mortar should be used for this purpose.

Spark screens are desirable if the location is in a wooded area or close to flammables. Rust resistant wire mesh having openings from one-half inch to five-eighths of an inch is used. Top of the screen should be at least twelve inches above the chimney cap.

Clearances. Fireplace and chimney walls should be separated from combustible material as follows: Framing members, two-inch airspace. Airspace should be fire-stopped at floor level with extension of ceiling finish, strips of asbestos board or other non-combustible material. Subfloor and flooring—three-quarter-inch airspace.

Surround. Combustible material should not be within three and one-half inches of the sides of a fireplace opening. Combustible material above (mantel) and projecting more than 1-1/2 inches in front of the fireplace opening shall be placed at least twelve inches above the opening.

Reinforcement. In earthquake areas (Map) masonry chimneys and fireplaces should be reinforced and anchored to the frame as follows:

Vertical Bars

Chimney Area (sq. in.)	No. of Bars	Size of Bar
Less than 300	4	No. 3
300 or over	4	No. 4

Install reinforcing full height of chimney, hooked into footing and chimney cap. Unless joints are welded, bars shall be installed without splices.

Reinforcing should be placed at corners of chimney in mortar joints between inner and outer course of eight inch walls or installed in two inches of cement grout between masonry and flue lining.

Horizontal Bars. No. 2 bars, twenty-four inches o.c. embedded in mortar joints, and

No. 3 bars at chimney cap and each plane of anchorage.

Anchorage. Anchor chimneys which are entirely or partly outside of exterior walls to structures at each floor line six feet or more above grade and at the upper ceiling or roof line.

2" MINIMUM

A FINISHED, CAPPED CHIMNEY WITH A HOOD

Finished chimney with hood.

FACE OF CHIMNEY (high Side)

LEVEL

"A"

4" MIN. FOR SLOPES 5", 12" AND OVER

3" MIN. FOR SLOPES UNDER 5" AND 12"

FLASHING SHALL BE CARRIED UP TO A POINT LEVEL WITH POINT "A" BUT NOT LESS THAN 1-1/2 TIMES SINGLE EXPOSURE

Flashing for chimneys thirty inches in width or less where no saddle is required.

BLOCKING AND SUPPORT

ROOF SHEATHING

SADDLE FRAMING

Chimney flashing and saddle (cricket) framing details.

FLUE LINING

COUNTER FLASHING BUILT INTO JOINT

CHIMNEY CAP — Concrete, metal, stone or other non-combustible, water-proof material.

CRICKET OR SADDLE

67

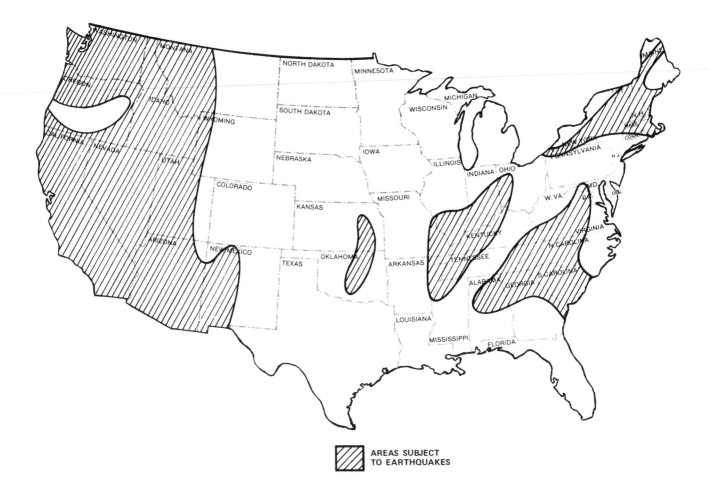

AREAS SUBJECT
TO EARTHQUAKES

Anchorage should consist of one-quarter-inch steel straps or equivalent reinforcing bars anchored to chimney masonry and to structural members of framework.

Construction

Two methods are generally used. In the first, the rough brickwork is completed from foundation to chimney top, leaving the construction of the firebox, hearth, smoke chamber, and chimney face for later, after the roof is on the building and more skilled hands are available. In the second method (more efficient), the fireplace is nearly completed as the work progresses, possibly leaving only the surround and outer hearth to be completed later. Either method will produce a successful fireplace.

Construction should follow detailed plans provided by the architect or fireplace equipment manufacturer.

Hearth. The hearth can be built on a reinforced concrete slab cantilevered out from the fireplace to support the outer hearth. This makes the hearth completely independent of the floor construction. In a variation of this, the outer hearth is supported by a brick arch springing from the foundation wall. Where the cantilever method is

Chimney reinforcement is tied into footing bars.

used, one-half-inch steel reinforcing bars form a grid ten to twelve inches on center. The steel should be about one inch from the top of the 3-1/2-inch slab and the slab is keyed into the back wall of the fireplace. Combustible forms and centering should be removed.

A slab may also be constructed with brick and mortar. Ribbed metal lath serves as the form and is laid in the mortar on top of the brick walls of the chimney base and supported at the projecting end by a temporary form.

On the metal lath is placed a bed of type M mortar deep enough to cover the ribs. This is followed at once by the placement of the brick on edge one-half inch apart without mortar. The joints should then be filled with cement mortar grout and the reinforcing bars set in place, pressing them down into position about one and one-half inches below the top surface.

Another, simpler method is used in some parts of the country. "T" irons are used to support brick which constitutes the sub-hearth. The "T" irons rest on the front foundation wall and then on a 2 x 4 ledger nailed to the face of the header in the fireplace opening. Although this method relies to some small extent on the support of the outer hearth from the floor joist, we have never seen an unsatisfactory installation of this type, and it is far less expensive.

Reinforcement bars at firebox level

Reinforcing bars at flue level

Anchor tie at roof line

Method of building a fireplace where firebox is built after chimney construction. Note lintel over smoke chamber and support for breast lintel to be installed later. With this method of construction, the entire fireplace front may be torn out at some future date for remodeling without endangering the structure. Note also the support for the flue lining.

69

Labels on the diagram:
fire-clay flue liner
*2" min. clearance for wood trimmer at chimney breast
chimney - 4" solid masonry (min) if flue liner is used
wood trimmer bm
support flue-liner.
parge smoke chamber with fire-clay mortar (refractory mortar). parging may be omitted if wall thickness is 8" solid masonry.
2" min*
3½"
adjustable damper.
lining of fire-brick (may be laid 2" way) shall extend full width of throat
8" min
2" min
16" min. outer hearth
8" min
inner hearth
8" min. total thickness
8" min. foundation wall
brick arch optional

Construction Details (Federal Housing Administration)

INNER HEARTH

"T" IRONS

BRICK

Simple hearth construction.

Firebox. Firebrick is laid in fire clay mortar with a maximum joint thickness of one-fourth inch. When laid the two-inch way (on edge) the firebox will need to be eight inches thick. Without the firebrick it should be twelve inches thick.

Firebrick and facing brick should be tied to rough masonry with galvanized steel brick ties.

Flue Lining. First flue liner should be supported by a ledge provided in masonry at the top of the smoke chamber.

Flue lining should be installed ahead of the construction of the chimney so it is carried up, carefully bedding one on the other in mortar with close fitting joints left smooth on the inside.

Where two flues adjoin each other in the same chimney, stagger joints at least seven inches or install wythe (four-inch course of brick bonded into chimney walls).

Where more than two flues are located in the same chimney, install a four-inch wythe bonded into the chimney separating flues into groups of one or two.

Where diagonal offsets are necessary in flue lining, bevel the edges of the liner at change in direction to insure smooth, tight joints.

Chimney Offset. Masonry chimneys may be offset at a slope of not more than four inches in twenty-four inches but not more than one third of the dimension of the chimney in the direction of the offset.

Changes in Size or Shape of Chimney should not be made within a distance of six inches above or below roof joists or rafters. It is sometimes desirable to increase the size of the chimney before it penetrates the roof line, for aesthetic reasons. Dummy flues are often provided in the enlarged chimney.

Hooded Fireplaces

Metal hoods add drama, and because the metal is heated and radiates heat into the room, they often increase heating efficiency.

Some hooded fireplaces are simply disguised conventional fireplaces with decorative metal over the opening. The standards of flue area, etc., given earlier apply to these fireplaces.

Other hooded fireplaces require special design by a competent fireplace designer or one of the manufacturers of custom hoods. Although the same principles apply, they must be worked out in different ways.

Some hooded fireplaces, local codes permitting, can be built without a heavy foundation and masonry chimney. A firebrick hearth and firewall are built right over the flooring and the flue is provided by one or more patent chimneys. Since the computed opening of most hooded fireplaces is much greater than other types, the area of flue or flues must be proportionately greater. Code requirements of the Uniform Building Code are given in Chapter 7.

Country club fireplace in large scale, with copper hood.

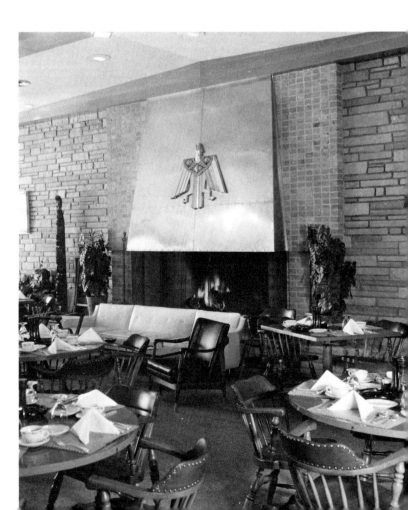

Relaxed dining is encouraged by handsome hooded fire.

71

6. Heat Circulating Fireplaces

The all metal heating type fireplace serves as a form for building an efficient fireplace with any desired exterior trim treatment. Air inlets or outlets that provide heat circulation (shown on the side) can be extended to other rooms, as well as artistically treated in the finished trim. (Majestic)

More than three hundred years of experiment have been devoted to the problem of going beyond the masonry fireplace and conserving heat ordinarily wasted up the chimney. The first step in this direction came about forty years ago with the introduction of the circulator fireplace.

Your masonry fireplace gives you only the radiated heat from the fire. A circulator fireplace gives you the radiated heat from the fire, plus the other kind—the circulated, convection heated air—greatly increasing the value received from the fuel you have paid for.

For the summer cottage, for the hunting cabin, or a between-season home heating system, or simply for use on those days when quick warmth will feel good but the use of the furnace is not quite justified, the circulator will pay for itself. In colder climates, the circulating fireplace will pay its small additional cost in reduction of fuel used by the main heating system. An additional advantage of this form of fireplace is its pre-built nature permitting ease of installation by the do-it-yourselfer or unskilled workman. This approach eliminates much of the measuring, checking, and guesswork involved in the construction of a conventional masonry fireplace. At the same time, the circulator retains the conventional appearance and charm.

How They Work

Like a warm-air furnace, circulators have double-wall construction. The inner steel wall surrounds the fire chamber as does the firebrick in a masonry fireplace.

Between the inner and outer walls is an air chamber. Air comes into this chamber through grilles at floor level, is heated by contact with the walls of the fireplace, and discharged through registers to the interior of the home. Additional heating efficiency can be obtained by adding fans to the warm air ducts which also permits the heating of a greater area.

An example of the greater heat extraction from a circulator follows. A typical thirty-six-inch width of fireplace front opening has approximately one thousand square inches of area through which the heat radiates. A modern circulator of similar size will have nearly three thousand additional square inches of steel surface exposed either to the fire or the hot products of combustion. These steel surfaces heat the air passed over them by convection and pass it on to the room—or even adjacent rooms—through a system of strategically located intake and outlet ducts and grilles.

Typical Circulating Fireplace. Drawing shows how cold air is drawn in the bottom, is heated between the two steel walls, and moves out the top.

Architectural Planning

Circulating fireplaces can be located in any location that a conventional masonry fireplace may occupy. Their location on an interior wall may be dictated by the desire to heat two or more rooms from the several ducts available.

Circulators are available from some manufacturers as corner models, right and left hand and as through wall units opening on two rooms. In conventional fireplaces of this type, an extremely high percentage of the heat is lost up the chimney. With a circulator a good deal of this can be captured, and at the same time the unique charm of this type of fireplace is retained. Manufacturer's instructions about draft, flue size, chimney cap, etc., should be closely followed.

The placement of grilles often affects the appearance of circulators. In many cases, outlet grilles are located in the upper masonry of the fireplace front. Should some other location be preferred architecturally, projection of the fireplace from the plane of the wall leaves an inconspicuous side position available for them. Shelving may further disguise their presence.

COOL AIR INLET
AIR PASSES THROUGH
GRILLE IN CLOSET DOOR

HOT METAL
BACK & SIDES
HEAT AIR

RADIANT HEAT
IN THIS ROOM

CIRCULATING
FIREPLACE USED
TO HEAT ROOMS
DIRECTLY IN BACK

73

Corner model heat circulator with unique method of forming air inlets and outlets. (Superior Fireplace Co.)

Ingenuity can often mask front-opening grilles. Latticed brickwork areas or stone baffles adorning the front at points of discharge have proved decorative and unobtrusive. Many other unique methods have been used, although the standard metal grilles are not necessarily offensive in appearance.

Construction

We should remember that the circulator is furnished by the manufacturer as a form for the masonry, not a supporting structure. The rules given elsewhere for footings, reinforcement, etc., of masonry fireplace construction still apply. The manufacturer's instructions furnished with the unit should be religiously followed.

Size and thickness of footing should be governed by local conditions and codes. Firebrick, with ash-dump (if used), is laid in the hearth area. An extended hearth of at least eight inches on each side of the fireplace opening and

with a minimum projection of sixteen inches must be provided. The hearth may be either raised or flush with the floor. A raised hearth may have provision for cold air intake under the hearth. In "tight" buildings provision should be made for combustion air by a ventilating brick in the ash-pit or other arrangement.

The fireplace unit is set in place on the hearth, and fastened to the hearth masonry. If required by the manufacturer, fiberglass or rock wool should cover the outside of the unit, and masonry should not contact the steel. Provide inlets and outlets as called for by instructions.

When masonry surround is complete, chimney should be built as described elsewhere in this book. Leave one-half inch or more space between metal and first flue tile.

In addition to the advantages of circulating fireplaces previously mentioned, we may say:

They take the guesswork out of fireplace building, affording a correctly formed interior.

They save the expense of expert fireplacing brickwork.

They insure a proper damper size and location.

They provide a good smokeless fireplace, a cheerful fire, and heat that circulates to the far parts of the room.

74

Large circulator in California Camp Fire Girls clubhouse. Cool air inlets are in the ends of the raised hearth and warm air outlets in sides of custom metal hood. (Superior Fireplace Co.)

Circulator fireplace with air inlets and outlets of spaced masonry. Wood box to the right opens through the exterior wall, so it can be filled with logs from the rear. (Superior Fireplace Co.) (below)

7. Pre-BUILT FirePLaCes

With all the appearances of a conventional wood-burning fireplace, this all-metal prefabricated corner model woodburning fireplace, complete with all-metal flue and simulated brick chimney top, can be easily installed in any home without special footings, foundation or masonry. (Majestic)

Esthetically, the traditional masonry fireplace, whether massive or petite, continues to be preferred over other types. However, the development of the Franklin stove and heat circulating fireplaces has been followed in recent years by the introduction of factory-built fireplaces requiring little of the high cost labor and hard-to-find skills required in masonry fireplacing.

Now it is possible to install a wood-burning fireplace without any concrete footings, without a masonry chimney and without relying on the fast-disappearing skills of masons whose hourly wages continue to climb out of proportion to the consumer's ability to pay.

Pre-built fireplaces are of two basic types: the conventional-appearing fireplace which is usually built into a wall (we call it a "built in pre-built") and the metal fireplace, usually freestanding, which makes no pretence of looking traditional. Both types usually employ prefabricated flues although on occasion they can be vented into existing chimneys.

Do It Yourself?

Pre-builts offer many advantages for installation by homeowners in existing or summer homes. The fact that no foundation is required permits the fireplace to be located anywhere the homeowner wishes. Upstairs or down, if you follow the manufacturer's installation instructions, you can be assured of a low cost, trouble free fireplace. The completeness of the package makes buying a one stop operation with responsibility falling on only one supplier.

Built in Pre-Builts

These package fireplaces come complete from the factory to the builder's specifications. Damper, fire screen, hearth, hearth extension, surround, chimney, chimney housing and cap, together with easily understood instructions, may all be included.

Pre-builts have major national and regional code approvals. However, it is well to check with the local code

Various applications of prebuilt fireplaces. (Heatilator Fireplaces)

involved before completing plans. "Zero clearance" approval of this type of fireplace means that most components may be installed directly on the subfloor and against wood framing. This is accomplished by insulation or by having multiple walls providing air spaces through which outside air circulates to keep outer surfaces safely cool.

These fireplaces are available as front opening models and as right- or left-hand corner models. Installation can be made projecting into the room, flush with the wall or with a raised hearth. Prefabricated flue may be angled around upper story fireplaces or other obstructions. In this manner, installations may be made in multiple housing with identical floor plans on successive floors.

As with conventional masonry fireplaces, the hearth, of incombustible material, should extend a minimum of sixteen inches from the front and eight inches on each side of the opening. Any of the conventional materials may be used for the hearth, slate, brick, ceramic tile, terra cotta tile, etc. Installation of these materials can be made directly on the subfloor, usually without special support.

This conventional appearing wood-burning fireplace illustrates how the modern, all-metal prefabricated fireplace can be finished with any preference of exterior trim; as well as completely installed without masonry. Note woodbox on right. (Majestic)

77

Metal fireplace designed for a corner installation. Brick provides fireproofing as well as decoration. (Malm Fireplaces, Inc.)

Hearth extensions are optionally available from the manufacturer.

Surround may be any of the common materials, including brick. Of course, the rule about combustible materials, no closer than three and one-half inches to the side of the opening, must be followed. Mantels of combustible materials projecting over one and one-half inches must be at least twelve inches above the opening.

Manufacturers have a standard black glass surround available. Walls around the fireplace may be given the massive masonry feeling by applying well designed plastic stone or brick. Real brick and stone (one-half inch thick) is available in sheets which can be applied to the fireplace area. Mortar is tuck pointed in joints after application.

Metal Fireplaces

Metal fireplaces feature the greatest flexibility in location together with a minimum cost. They can vary from the simplest sheet metal firehood to expensive, factory-finished copper hoods with special-built masonry hearths. The metal hoods radiate heat on all sides and are thus more efficient as room heaters than most masonry fireplaces.

To eliminate long remembered burns, some models are made with two and three wall thicknesses through which air circulates. These act like a furnace much as circulating fireplaces do. Clearance to combustible surfaces varies from zero to twenty-eight inches. Underwriters label or manufacturer's instructions should be checked on this point.

Hoods

Free standing, open on all sides, hoods have a tendency to smoke unless there is an adequate draft in the fireplace. The sudden opening of a window or door or even walking rapidly past can disturb the draft.

One solution is to pipe air from outside the house directly into or in front of the hearth or firepit. A fan placed at the top of the flue is another way to insure proper draft.

Since this type of hood has a rather large opening (360 degrees) the size of the flue should be ample. Also, some

Colorful metal fireplace with pecan paneling background. Box containing marble chips is hearth. (Georgia-Pacific)

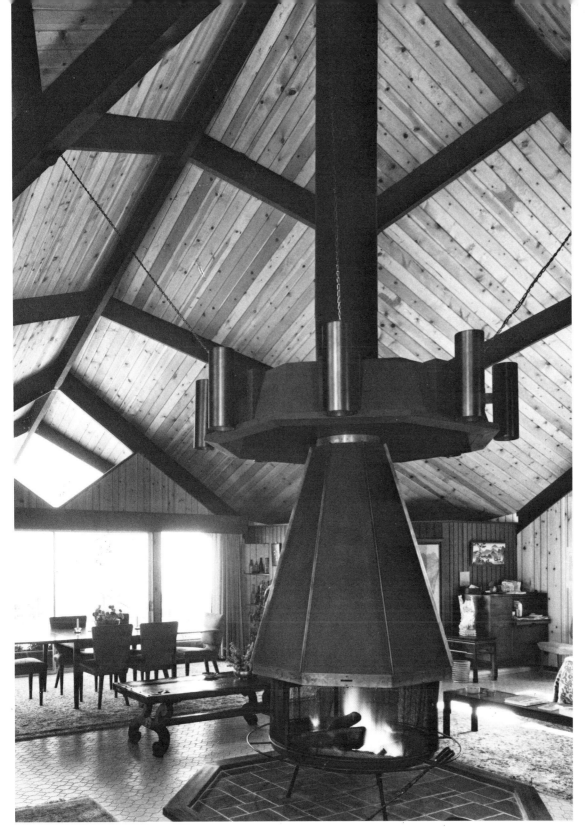

Free-standing hood is center of attraction in large room.
(Goodwin of California)

extra height to the flue will help insure the draft. To determine the area, measure the circumference of the hood and multiply by the distance from the firepit to the rim of the hood. The flue area should be at least one-eighth this size, and a metal disc damper should be provided.

The following are the requirements of the Universal Building Code (1971) regarding hoods:

"Metal hoods used as part of a fireplace or barbecue shall be not less than No. 19 gauge copper, galvanized steel, or other equivalent corrosion-resistant ferrous metal with all seams and connections of smokeproof unsoldered constructions. The hood shall be sloped at an angle of 45° or less from the vertical and shall extend horizontally at least 6 inches beyond the limits of the firebox. Metal hoods shall be kept a minimum of 18 inches from combustible materials unless approved for reduced clearances."

Architects and homeowners are well advised to stick with standard, proprietary factory built units of this type which are warranted to work by the manufacturer. For more expensive installations, some firms make custom built units.

Standard Metal Fireplaces

These units have the advantage of having been proved in many installations and usually bear the Underwriter's Label for further safety and local code acceptance. Most units are available with companion flue, housing, and chimney cap assemblies.

Although some metal woodburning fireplaces can theoretically be placed on their legs over any type of floor, a hearth of concrete, brick, ceramic tile or other non-combustible material is recommended. Often a box containing sand, pebbles, or marble chips is used and can be as decorative as it is economical.

A firescreen is most desirable, as is the ash drawer provided with some units. The ash drawer will eliminate much of the after-fire cleanup.

Manufacturers of these units make them in many colors from the economical stove black to many bright porcelain colors. The colorful porcelain on steel is easy to keep clean.

Included in the group of standard metal fireplaces are several makes of the Franklin stoves and the traditional pot-bellied stove. Franklin stoves may be either free standing or placed in a masonry niche.

Metal fireplaces should be warmed up slowly because the rapid expansion of metal parts may cause warping of sheet metal or crazing of porcelain finish.

Installation of Pre-Built Fireplace (Heatilator Fireplaces)

Pre-built flue housing with simulated brick. (Heatilator Fireplaces)

The straight line styling of this free-standing wood-burning fireplace makes it especially versatile, both as to room location and room decor. Available for either top venting as shown or with rear outlet for mounting on the wall. (Majestic)

Traditional Franklin stove. (Washington Stove Works)

8. ELECTRIC AND GAS FIREPLACES

Wall hung electric fireplace. (Fasco)

If you are an apartment dweller, yet a fireplace lover, if you cannot afford a fireplace in your new home, or should you abhor the chore of cleaning the hearth, keeping it supplied with wood, and periodically cleaning the ashpit, you may find an answer in electric or gas fireplaces. They are available in a wide assortment of types and costs from a number of manufacturers.

Electric and gas fireplace equipment can be installed on existing masonry hearths, incorporated into most types of pre-built fireplaces, and some types you can even take with you when you move! The charm, beauty and warmth of a fireplace can be yours wherever you are.

Electric Fireplaces

Electric fireplaces are available in many types. The simplest do not provide heat, although they have log sets which flicker and glimmer like real logs. These use regular house current and can simply be plugged into a wall outlet. Others provide heat through electric heating elements, radiating heat into the room much as wood logs.

Electric log sets for installation in existing fireplaces are also available. You can have them with or without heating elements.

The ultimate electric fireplace provides forced air heat in response to a thermostat installed on a wall on the opposite side of the room. These sometimes require three-wire outlets much like an electric range. Heat output on some models is as much as 6000 BTU's, enough to heat one or more rooms.

Electric models are available which can be moved about like a piece of furniture. These are complete with wood mantel, simulated brick hearth and facing, and may even include a complete set of fireplace furnishings. The decor of the room is not fixed; the fireplace can be moved from wall to wall, room to room, and you can even take it along when you move.

Safety is a feature in electric fireplaces. You need only be sure that the outlet you plug into has adequate amperage and that the unit you buy carries an Underwriters Label.

Gas Fireplaces

The same advantages of lowered cost, beauty, and simplicity of installation are typical of the modern gas fireplace.

Electric fireplace unit is complete with hearth and mantel. Can be moved like furniture. (Fasco)

Showing how a compact gas-fired fireplace by means of a choice of available screen assemblies, can be given the illusion of a large size, realistic wood-burning fireplace when used in larger rooms. Lighted by push-button and vented with prefabricated metal flue. (Majestic)

Electric fireplace with wood mantel and screen.
(Readybuilt)

Their variety ranges from complete room-heating units to gas log sets for already existing fireplaces where wood is unavailable or too expensive.

The factory-built gas-fired fireplace saves on construction costs because no masonry or brick foundations are required. Installation requires no special tools or craftsmen in many cases. Pre-assembled units fit in place on the existing floor and a carpenter merely has to frame the unit in. Finish trim can be selected to match the decor of the room, or units complete with finish trim or with panels are available.

These units are manufactured for both natural and L.P. gas. The only precaution the buyer should take is to purchase only units which meet the standards of the American Gas Association. It is also wise to check local building code specifications.

One popular compact unit is no deeper than a bookcase and thus can fit in a small apartment or mobile home. At the other extreme, there are models which contain both a gas fireplace and a self-contained thermostatically controlled heating unit which can be used separately or together to heat completely a large room.

Safety pilots, push button controls for instant firing, blowers to circulate heat throughout rooms, all are offered the homeowner interested in gas fireplaces. Many pilots are self-generating and do not have to connect into a house or building electrical system.

Units are prepared for 1/2-inch or 3/8-inch gas plumbing through the floor, side, or back to the gas control valve. They can be vented with standard type B gas vent or into an existing approved flue. The gas vent is much more economical than those provided for solid fuel prebuilts.

Gas fireplaces can be used in multiple housing. In high-rise buildings the required flues fit easily between studs into a normal four-inch wall with only the usual elementary sheet metal duct work. Where a flue is not already available, factory-made prefabricated vent packages can be supplied with the fireplace.

Homeowners with existing fireplaces who are interested in switching to gas log sets will find these vastly changed from the early models which frequently were justly characterized as "artificial" looking. Modern manufacturers offer an infinite variety of log sets simulating various woods and giving a realistic, cheery flame. These woods range from the more conventional white birch and oak through twisted cypress to the more exotic effect of simulated tiki and manzanita log sets.

It must be stressed that gas log sets, if not part of a factory-manufactured complete fireplace unit, should be operated only in a vented fireplace with a chimney free of any obstructions and with the damper fully open.

Luxurious is the word for this instant on, instant off remote controlled gas fireplace. (American Gas Association)

9. THE LASTING LURE OF OPEN FIRE COOKERY

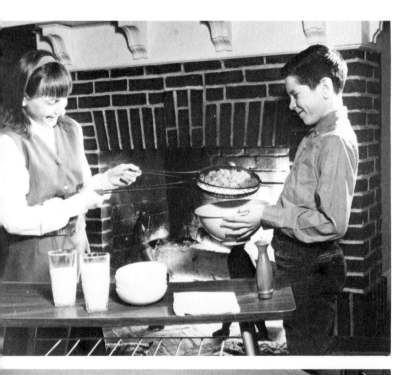

When the old fashioned nineteenth century picnic, with its potato salad, sandwiches and pie, encountered the twentieth century masculine appetite for more solid fare (and less fattening), an era of open fire cookery was born. Open cookery has increased in popularity and has been refined so that it is now a delight to millions of Americans of all ages.

Grilling or roasting was found to be a joyful experience, the only regret being that the climate of much of America forbade enjoyment of outdoor meals almost half of the year. Again, in recent years the addition of air conditioning to many new homes has tended to move the barbecue indoors.

The Barbecue Moves Indoors

So, open fire cookery was put on a twelve month basis by the birth of the indoor barbecue. By indoor, we include barbecues located in enclosed porches, lanai, or in special shelters constructed near or adjoining the home. Family rooms, kitchens, and recreation rooms in basements or elsewhere are also popular. Kitchen barbecues are now available to fit right into the counter tops, with built in ventilation. Equipment is available to turn the fireplace into a barbecue, either with charcoal or the regular log fire.

Barbecues are no substitute for the ordinary routine of kitchen operation. They represent something special, something particularly in demand when guests are to be entertained or when the family is in a holiday mood—and particularly when father feels the impulse to exercise his talents as a chef.

A Masculine Institution

We note this because it is doubtful that barbecue cookery would persist, but for the talents and zeal of male volunteers. No one claims that woman could not learn to grill a steak over a charcoal fire, but few have seen anything of the sort—"women's lib" notwithstanding.

Corn Popper. Here is a fireplace accessory that works over glowing coals and without oil. (Androck)

Custom barbecue with metal hood encourages participation of the consumer. (Goodwin of California)

This modern barbecue unit, that may be installed into the standard wood or metal kitchen cabinet, brings barbecue cooking conveniently indoors—for year around enjoyment. These units are available for using charcoal, gas or electricity as fuel and also in a style to drop in a counter top with front concealed. (Majestic)

For the contemporary home, a barbecue grill set into an immaculate ceramic tile counter and wall makes for easy entertainment. (American Olean Tile Company)

Fireplace detail showing patio barbecue incorporated into chimney stack. Not to scale. (Garlinghouse Plan Service, Topeka, Kansas)

Choosing an Outdoor Location

If we begin with the open flame cooking device in its original outdoor setting, we are confronted with the problem of location. It must not be too far from the rear entrance of the home, or the carrying of fuel, food and utensils becomes a chore. In fact, many excellent barbecues have been built against the outer wall of a house, utilizing the house chimney stack. In other instances, a garden or lawn site at a moderate distance from the house will be favored. Such a project should include visualizing the complete setting—benches and tables for the diners, plantings of shrubs or vines to afford privacy.

Getting Started Outdoors

A competent mason who enters into the spirit of your project is a good investment. However, many men with a knack for outdoor tasks will prefer to wield the trowel themselves.

The first problem in either case is that of a proper foundation so that the structure will not settle or sag. Many prefer to excavate below the frost line, pouring a six-inch concrete foundation. However, many excellent outdoor fireplaces are supported on the "floating slab" principle. A shallow excavation is made and a concrete slab is poured with steel reinforcing installed. Six-inch by six-inch wire road mesh will do. Depending on the size of the barbecue, the slab should be from four to six inches thick and should extend at least four inches outside the boundaries of the fireplace.

Install Tested Equipment

In the case of amateur installations outdoors, there is sometimes a temptation to improvise metal features. A grill will be made from parallel steel rods, cemented tightly in place. The rods soon warp or sag. Expansion loosens the masonry bond. Much better to rely on a unit manufactured for the purpose by one of the reputable manufacturers listed in the back of the book. Follow manufacturers instructions and allow for expansion.

No single unit is likely to satisfy all the desires of the open-fire chef so plan your equipment requirements with foresight. Dutch ovens, powered or hand operated spits, adjustable fire levels, and cleanout doors are among the items to be considered.

A chimney is not always necessary. If you plan to burn only charcoal, the walls around the metal units are sufficient. However, if either wood or coal is the fuel to be used, the barbecue-fireplace should have a chimney. It is also good thinking to cap the chimney to keep out rain and snow and possibly a screen to arrest sparks from wood fires.

Indoor Barbecue Problems

If your open-fire cooking installation is to be in a new house, you probably have consulted with the architect about many features. Two things should not be overlooked—having the whole cooking area properly vented to carry off fumes, and second, the need for table space adjoining the cooking area to manipulate pots, pans, and utensils. Often we have encountered cases where the cooking unit was recessed in a narrow space at table height, but with no chance for the chef to maneuver.

Overhead view of 16' x 16' sun court showing sunken fire pit for both warmth and cooking. (California Redwood Association)

Do It Yourselfers may order plans for this barbecue from Craft Patterns, Elmhurst, Illinois, 60126. (65¢)

Franklin stove equipped with optional barbecue grill makes it into a dual purpose unit. (U S Stove, Inc.)

Kitchen fireplace makes this room into an all-purpose room with a new personality. (Marsh Wall Products)

Circulating Fireplace incorporates indoor barbecue unit on same chimney stack. (Superior Fireplace Co.)

10. HINTS ON TENDING
AN OPEN FIRE

Some people have an instinct for fire tending; some gain fire knowledge by slow experience. Our grandfathers had fire duties from early youth, while the current crop of householders includes many who never acquired practice until a fuel shortage drove them to fire-lighting duties.

For their benefit we may say that the nineteenth century chore boy learned three stages in producing a fire, represented by the paper, the kindling wood, and the actual fuel, which might be coal or hard wood.

The match produced the flame; the paper spread it; the kindling held it, and produced heat enough to ignite the fuel with a fire that would last.

The Question of Draft

Tight homes have made the draft question so acute of late that it is a good thing to determine whether there is a decided down-draft in the chimney before starting. Wet a finger and hold it under the fireplace throat. If it is cold on the upper side, the draft is coming down. Starting a fire in that fireplace will result in a smoke filled room. Air is coming into the house through the chimney and may be consumed in combustion of the furnace or exhausted by a kitchen or bathroom ventilating fan. If opening a window a few inches or providing some other air input does not reverse the down draft, see the following chapter to find the trouble.

In a new home, it will pay to check the effect of ventilating fans being turned on while a fire is in the hearth. If there is no way to replace this air, except down the chimney, your fireplace will smoke and ashes may be drawn onto the hearth, even through a screen.

Selecting the Fuel

Wood logs are most desirable for use in an open fireplace, though some firebuilders prefer to use coal, charcoal, or compressed sawdust logs. A wood fire is required to start other fuels.

Logs are usually available in the twenty-four-inch size. A smaller size, sixteen inches in length, is called stove wood. Larger logs to three feet and longer are available for king-sized fireplaces. Logs may be split or whole, although split logs start burning faster.

Well seasoned hardwoods such as beech, hickory, oak, maple, and most fruitwoods are preferable to softwoods such as pine and evergreens, although these make excellent kindling.

The softwoods usually burn too fast, but for this reason, they may be desirable if you want a roaring fire "right now."

Apple and hickory give a pleasant aroma. Hickory is preyed upon by carpenter bugs that may infest the premises. Elm logs that have been killed by the Dutch Elm disease are to be avoided to minimize contamination of other elms in your neighborhood. Madrone, manzanita, and eucalyptus are used in the west.

Kindling can be any species, split into little sticks less than three-fourths of an inch thick. Branches accumulated from tree pruning on your property will do the job well when dry. Pine boughs saved from your Christmas tree work well as do pine cones used in conjunction with kindling wood.

Cannel coal is one of the popular coals for fireplace use. It is the next thing to an oil-bearing shale, ignites quickly, sputters a good deal and makes a lot of ash. A fire screen is good caution when burning cannel but a screen diminishes heat and mars enjoyment.

Kentucky coals have earned a fine reputation as fireplace coal. They ignite easily, burn brightly, with a minimum of fine powder-like ash without clinkers. There are other kinds of bituminous coals that burn acceptably in open fires.

Of course, charcoal is favored for cooking in the fireplace and some fire tenders prefer it or charcoal mixed with wood for their regular fires. Charcoal radiates about twice as much heat as wood and charcoal briquets are even better. Odorless, invisible carbon monoxide is given off by charcoal, so adequate ventilation should always be provided.

Ocean driftwood will burn with a blue and lavender fire. Other colorful fires can be produced by soaking firewood, pine cones, or charcoal in various salt solutions. Use strontium chloride or nitrate for a red flame. Common table salt (sodium chloride) makes a yellow fire. Green and blue flames are produced by copper chloride.

Avoid the use of scrap lumber (except for kindling), refuse or Christmas wrappings as these may produce a great many sparks which could become a fire hazard.

Laying the Fire

Much of the literature of New England must have been produced in front of log fires, if we draw inference from continual allusions to the fire and to fire lighting. There was (and is) a positive ritual of back logs and fore logs, of preferences in wood.

Let us see if we can reduce these dogmas to general principles. We have seen that a fire must (1) be lit, (2) be spread, and (3) be held until general ignition takes place. The final stage of fire tending is to conserve it and keep the fuel from burning up too rapidly.

Ready for logs

Andirons are usually placed twelve to sixteen inches apart, centered on the hearth. If you build a fire daily, leave some of yesterday's ashes, brushed together as a foundation for today's bed of coals. Place three or four inches of twisted or crumpled newspaper on the hearth between the andirons. Arrange kindling criss-cross on the papers. If a fire basket is used, the kindling fire may be placed in or under the basket, allowing air space.

Set up two four- to five-inch logs across the andirons with the thickest, longest, or greenest about one-half of an inch away from the back. Leave a few inches between the back log and the front log (preferably split). Place a split log on top, arranged so it leaves room for the flames to come through.

Function of a Back Log

If your wood supply contains some pieces that are hard to burn, perhaps green, do not be disappointed. They make fine back logs. The back log lies against the back of the fireplace. You lean split pine or faggots against it in kindling your fire. It makes a counter-surface for livelier-burning wood and helps to hold the body of the blaze forward where it will do the most good.

Wood that is fairly green can be burned after the fire is well under way, especially if there is a good bed of coals. It should be split finer than is necessary with dry, seasoned wood.

English Fire-Laying Method

Here is a method of laying a wood fire much used in England. Newspapers are first crumpled between the andirons, then two logs are laid parallel with a space between, over the paper. Kindling is laid across these logs, spread about an inch apart, with a few sticks standing vertically down into the paper. Then the third log is placed on top, parallel with the bottom logs. This arrangement creates a quick flame with good draft between the logs.

It is said that the English have developed this system because wood is very scarce and it is considered essential to have a nice, newly laid fire blazing in the hall or guest room immediately when a visitor arrives—as essential as their little courtesy of polishing shoes overnight.

Fuel Around the Flame

The commonest error of neophytes with a fireplace is to try to burn one log of wood at a time. Even two logs are apt to snuff out. Three units in your wood fireplace represent a practical minimum.

A twist of the key quickly creates a cheery, warm blaze without the use of kindling by the installation of a gas log lighter. (Canterbury Enterprises)

Two styles of Cape Cod lighters

Good fire-builders recognize that the growing flame needs the protection of fuel around it—that it thrives best when twisting upward between faggots or chunks that continually obstruct it, continually force it to twist and turn.

Before lighting the kindling, lay about one sheet of crumpled newspaper on the logs. Lighting this moments before lighting the kindling warms the flue and establishes a draft.

All Ready? Before you light the match:
MAKE SURE THE DAMPER IS WIDE OPEN!!

"Holding" a Wood Fire

Contrary to general belief a fire of coal or wood can be held overnight in a fireplace. First, leave a bed of coals with some unburned fuel on top, cover the fireplace open-

Electric firestarter

ing with a piece of sheet metal, except for three or four inches at the top. A little practice will bring gratifying results in conditions where this overnight fire is desirable.

Building a Coal Fire

Coal is a more stable fuel than wood and requires less attention, but it does not have the cheerful blaze of wood, although it is kindled in much the same manner as wood. If you have a good "grate" coal, the blaze will be well established in fifteen minutes, but it should not be crowded. The flue should be warmed gradually and each piece of coal placed carefully until a lively coal flame has been achieved.

Igniting Devices

To many city dwellers, the question of kindling wood is quite as acute as that of getting firewood. To them a mechanical lighting device makes sense.

A built-in gas fired log starter is often used for this purpose. An electric fire starter is also available. A Cape Cod lighter is a device with a metal handle and a head of absorbent fireclay which rests in a small kettle of kerosene. Removed and lighted it acts as a wick and ignites the coal or wood used as a fuel. However, the absorbent fire-

Unburned logs standing on end in back corners will soon go out.

clay becomes heated and if the fire does not soon ignite, do not re-immerse the lighter in the oil immediately or oil may explode.

Pouring gasoline or oil on the fire to get it started? Don't! Even charcoal lighter fluid should be used with care.

Use of Fire Tools

It is a sign of bad fire tending to lift a coal hod and throw a large part of its contents on the flame. Better to place each chunk where needed with the tongs, or to lift out moderate-sized shovelfuls with the fire shovel.

The poker should be used to rouse the flame by opening new draft passages among the embers and by rearranging the fuel. In the case of wood fires, there is repeated need to bring the unburned ends of logs into the center of the fire, and a poker, or tongs, makes easy work of this task. A brush is useful in cleaning the hearth or keeping the ashes in a neat pile. Some people like to use a bellows as a persuader for a lagging flame.

Operation of Damper

Make sure that the damper is wide open before you light your fire. Many fireplaces are operated with dampers constantly open. Dampers do not have to be constantly opened and closed in order to be of great value in promoting smooth discharge of smoke and arresting down-draft.

When the fire-builder has mastered other features of fireplace operation, he can begin experimenting to see how much his damper opening can be cut down, with his fuel, and save heat while discharging all the smoke. When only a bed of glowing coal remains, the damper can be brought nearest to a closed position. But be sure to open it before refueling with smoke-producing fuel.

Putting the Fire Out

Use a pair of fire tongs to stand any unburned logs on end in the back corners of the fireplace. They will soon go out and you will have some good kindling ready for the next fire. When retiring for the night, leave the damper open and the screen closed, to be sure that no chance ignition will cause trouble while you sleep.

11. Fireplace DIFFICULTIES

Their Prevention,
Diagnosis and Treatment

Properly constructed fireplaces burn warmly, cleanly, safely. Those owners who "guess all fireplaces smoke" are making the wrong guess. Yet faulty construction is common enough. Investigation nearly always reveals some basic fault in planning, or some mistake of execution or operation.

Causes of Smokiness

The great majority of complaints about fireplace operation are based on smoky operation. Here are some of the conditions and remedies that relate to smokiness.

❶ METAL HOOD
❸ SIDES NARROWED ❸
❹ BACK RELINED
❷ RAISED HEARTH

Fireplace too Large for Flue

The flue area should not be less than the area of the fireplace opening. Where too small to carry off products of combustion, remedy may be found in reducing the size of the opening. Some corrective workers (1) install a shallow hood of metal beneath the fireplace breast. This also helps in cases where the damper position is too low. (2) Other ways of reducing the opening are to raise the hearth by laying one or two courses of brick over the old hearth. (3) Where drastic reduction is needed narrow the sides of the opening.

Damper too Low

Smokiness often ensues because the damper has been installed with its front flange at the lower level of the front wall, serving as a support for the brickwork. The remedy is to lower the top of the opening by adding one or two courses of brick, resting on an angle lintel.

DAMPER TOO LOW

Lack of Combustion Air

Recent innovations in caulking and weather-stripping have made homes so tight that there are no air inlets to provide air for oxygen and for draft, such as every fire needs. The result is that the unlighted fireplace becomes an inlet for outdoor air. If the furnace, the cooking range and incinerator are lighted, there is a steady current of air down the fireplace chimney.

DON'T MAKE FLUE OPENING TOO SMALL FOR SIZE OF FIREPLACE OPENING

DON'T LEAVE OUT SMOKE CHAMBER

Then if the fireplace is lighted, the draft down the chimney is pretty sure to drive smoke out into the room. We have repeatedly investigated complaints of smoky fireplaces which proved to be due to lack of ventilation for the interior as a whole. Often opening a basement window an inch or two would cause the fire to burn brightly. The only answer to this type of fireplace trouble is ventilation—not merely for the fireplace, but for the furnace, incinerator, range, etc. It is a poor sort of progress that excludes air from interiors where people are supposed to live.

Leakage from Flue to Flue

Sometimes smoke will issue from a fireplace that has no fire in it. Search will show that flues have been placed side by side in the same stack without cementing the joints between units of flue lining. If a furnace fire is burning briskly, there is apt to be down-draft in the fireplace flue,

for reasons stated. Smoke will be sucked across through the uncemented flue lining joints and descend (providing principles outlined above are disregarded)—coming out of the fireplace. The remedy is to close such passages. Staggering units of the lining is a help.

Use of Perforated Brick

Where workmanship is good, there can be no objection to the use of perforated brick in chimney work. Where a job is carelessly done, the fact that brick is perforated may account for the emission of smoke at a point that cannot otherwise be accounted for. The fault, in such cases, is with the workmanship, not the material.

Leakage Impairs Draft

Where flue joints are uncemented and mortar in surrounding brickwork disintegrates, there is often a leakage of air into the chimney. This prevents the chimney from exercising the draft possibilities which its height would otherwise assure. The case is similar to that of trying to smoke a cigarette with a hole in the paper. Thorough pointing of the brickwork usually effects a cure.

Wind Deflected Down Chimney

The surroundings of a home may have a marked bearing on fireplace performance. If located at the foot of a bluff or hill, or if there are high trees close at hand, the result may be to deflect wind down the chimney in heavy gusts. A near-by high building has been known to produce the

same effect. The detail of a hooded chimney below the sketch of a house shows a common and efficient way of dealing with this difficulty. It may also be mentioned that carrying the flue lining a few inches above the brickwork, with a bevel of cement around it, is a recognized means of promoting clean exit of smoke from the flue. It minimizes wind eddies. The cement bevel also causes moisture to drain from the top and prevents frost troubles between linings and masonry.

"Pouring" from Flue to Flue

We have spoken of the case where down-draft from interior suction pulls smoke from the top of one flue down an

ADJUSTABLE CAP

CONTROL ARM

A new product has recently come on the market. It is a chimney cap, adjustable from the hearth, and eliminates the need for a damper; keeps the chimney closed when not is use, reducing heating and air conditioning costs; eliminates down drafts; keeps out wild intruders and provides instant up draft because the chimney is warm when the fire is started. The manufacturer claims that many of the problems described in this chapter can be cured by the use of this product. (The Chim-A-Lator Co.)

adjoining flue. Related to this is the case where vertical wind currents force smoke down an inactive flue as it emerges from an adjoining flue. One way to treat this is to carry the flues to different heights above the masonry. In other cases, multiple flues are capped, as shown. Note the bevel of cement which helps drainage and promotes clean emission of smoke.

Cases of Flue Leakage

There are various cases where smoke or odors will pervade a home through faulty chimney construction. One type of difficulty comes from the butting of open tile against a flue. Unless the joint of the flue is tight and remains so, it will emit smoke through the hollow tile, and may issue at a point remote from the fireplace and prompt a call for the fire department.

Proper Joint Practice

The safeguards against conditions cited are threefold—(1) Careful cementing of flue joints, space between flue lining and brickwork being filled with mortar. (2) Staggering of joints in adjoining flues, or at least four inches of well-cemented brick between flues. (3) Surrounding brickwork properly laid and joined.

Method of Sealing Joints

A method of closing uncemented flue joints without tearing out the chimney has been used with success in some instances. It involves the use of a traveling plug and fairly thin grout. As a plug, a canvas bag is sometimes employed, stuffed with rags or papers and weighted with bricks in the bottom. When lowered into a flue from the top, by means of a line or pole, it should fit fairly tight, but not too tight for motion. The method of use is to stop it just below the level of each flue joint and pour grout down the flue. When stopped by the plug, the grout flows into the open joint. After the joint appears filled, the plug may be lifted and lowered a few times, producing a swabbing effect. Then it is lowered to the succeeding joint and the operation repeated.

This operation should be carried out with careful eye to conditions in the fireplace below. If too much grout is passing the plug, it may pile up on the smoke shelf, drain into the fireplace and deface it, or, in hardening, may impair the working of the damper.

Flue Off Center

The flue should always take off from the center of the smoke chamber and, if a slope is necessary, it should occur above that point. When the flue takes off from one side, it produces uneven draft. Smoke travels sluggishly from the farther side of the fire area and is prone to eddy out into the room. Correction calls for rebuilding the smoke chamber and realigning of the flue.

Double Use of Fireplace Flue

Where kitchen stove, furnace or other appliance, uses the same flue as the fireplace, there is always a danger of smoking and draft disturbances. Each fireplace should have its own flue.

Flue Choked by Debris

The commonest form which this difficulty takes is the deposit of mortar, carelessly dropped down the chimney during construction. If the flue is straight, debris generally lodges on the smoke shelf and may impede the working of the damper. This condition may be corrected by disconnecting the control device, lifting out the valve plate and removing the debris through the fireplace throat. In case there are turns in the flue, debris may lodge at the angle and such debris is sometimes found to include broken pieces of brick and flue tile. In some instances such obstructions can be dislodged from above by a pole or weighted line and debris removed from the smoke shelf. More often it involves tearing out.

Choking at Base of Flue

The upper course of brick in the smoke chamber should offset just enough to afford support for the flue lining, without impinging on the area of the opening. Frequently it is found that bricks have been set in such a way as to reduce the area of the flue. The only remedy involves removing the obstruction. The same effect might be produced by a cap that chokes the outlet.

Sooty Fireplace Face

Should the face of your fireplace become stained with smoke and soot, clean it with a mild acid bleach, such as vinegar or acetic acid, or scour with strong soap and water. Stubborn stains can be scrubbed with a solution of hydrochloric (muriatic) acid. Rubber gloves, please! Do not use on stonework. It may also discolor some types of brick. Mixture is one part acid to ten parts water. Rinse off with water immediately. This treatment will also remove construction stains from mortar, etc.

Of course, if you avoid getting the fireplace dirty, you don't have to clean it. Avoid burning trash and paper in large amounts as your flue is not sized for this sudden load.

Flue Lining Out of Line

Sometimes careless masons fail to set flue lining with due alignment, leaving uneven joints, prone to cause leakage of smoke and fumes. In some instances where a slight change of direction in the flue is necessary, it is done—not by sloping the flue in the proper manner—but by successive offsets of vertical lining.

One Fireplace Below Another

Two fairly common mistakes in building a recreation room fireplace below a living room fireplace are—(1) Using one flue for both. (2) Taking off the flue for the lower fireplace at the side of the smoke chamber, in order to carry it around the fireplace above. The lower fireplace should be offset sufficiently so that a flue from the lower fireplace by-passes the upper one and reaches the chimney stack by a slope of not more than 7 inches to the foot. See design on Page 65.

Ashpit Clogged

Difficulty sometimes encountered in removing ashes from ashpits points to the need of making pits with uniform sectional areas and smooth walls. When pits or chutes are offset in passing a fireplace on a lower floor, all possible care must be taken to avoid roughness or sharp changes of direction. Wall leakage, particularly in the basement wall,

permits water to seep in and convert ashes into a soaked and tightly packed mass. The ashpit door should be centered at the base of the pit and be large enough to afford access, by poker, in freeing clogged masses near the base. More difficult conditions may call for tearing out masonry and treating obstructions.

Moisture and Frost Troubles

Because chimneys are subject to contrast of inner and outer temperatures, there is more tendency for mortar to

crack and disintegrate than in wall masonry. Natural gas fumes, which form a vapor, may escape through uncemented flue joints and augment the effect of moisture. Cottages left vacant during the winter are particularly subject to moisture and frost troubles.

Moisture in masonry is always a menace, because it freezes in cold weather and causes disintegration of mortar

and spalling of the brickwork. The greatest source of danger is the chimney top. There should be a smooth, impervious bevel of cement at the top, closing the joint between brickwork and lining. If this bevel cracks, and admits moisture between lining and brickwork, disintegration is rapid. The chimney becomes a menace because high winds may blow it down. Joint leakage is a lesser evil. Capping the flue as illustrated on Pages 67 and 98 is a safeguard against moisture entering the inside of the flue.

Chimneys should be kept under observation for the need of pointing, and their tops examined periodically. Mastic pointing is more effective than cement pointing because mastic adheres better and repels water. Roof cement makes an excellent pointing material.

Use of Fire Basket

Where a fire is built directly on the hearth, it has somewhat the effect of increasing the size of the fireplace opening, and a larger flue may be desirable. Conversely, installing a fire basket may cure trouble from an inadequate flue.

Where the breast of the fireplace is thick, trouble may result from placing the basket too far forward. In general it is safest to have the front of the basket no farther forward than the rear line of the breast. A little experimenting in basket position will show where it yields the most heat with minimum risk of smoke eddies.

Troubles Generally Avoidable

With comparatively rare exceptions, the troubles that owners suffer from their fireplaces are easily avoidable. It costs little, if anything, more to build a fireplace correctly than to build it badly. Against the varied array of difficulties we have mentioned must be counted the millions of fireplaces that operate to produce uniform warmth, cheer and contentment. Corrective work may involve considerable tearing out, but it is preferable to long endurance of an unsatisfactory fireplace.

INDEX

equipment manufacturers

Following is a list of Equipment Manufacturers and suppliers whose products came to the attention of the authors during research for this book. The list is not all-inclusive and there may be others who have escaped notice.

Androck
28 Union Street
Worcester, Mass. 01608   *D, Corn Popper*

Bennett-Ireland
23 State Street
Norwich, New York 13815   *D*

Canterbury Enterprises
6253 Hollywood Blvd.
Los Angeles, Calif. 90028   *Gas Log Lighters*

The Chim-A-Lator Co.
8824 Wentworth Ave., South
Minneapolis, Minn. 55420   *Chim-A-Lator*

Morton L. Clark, Inc.
2530 Manatee Ave.
West Bradenton, Fla. 33505   *H*

Condon-King Co.
5611 208th Ave. S.W.
Lynnwood, Wash. 98063   *C*

Dyna Manufacturing Co.
850 East 111th Place
Los Angeles, Calif. 90059   *H, G*

The Endeavour Periods, Inc.
1485 Berger Drive
San Jose, Calif. 95112   *F*

Fasco Industries, Inc.
255 N. Union Street
Rochester, New York 14605   *G*

Goodwin of California, Inc.
1075 Second St.
Berkeley, Calif. 94710   *Custom Hoods*

Hearth Shoppe Products Co.
P.O. Box 11
Oreland, Penn. 19705   *D*

Heatilator Fireplaces
Vega Industries, Inc.
Syracuse, New York 13205   *A, B, C, E, H*

Hewnrite Industries
5 Pecone Blvd.
Farmingdale, N.Y. 11735   *F*

Lincoln Steel Corp.
Box 1668
Lincoln, Neb. 68501   *B*

The Majestic Co. Inc.
Huntington, Ind. 46750   *A, B, C, D, E, G, H, I*

Malm Fireplaces, Inc.
368 Yolanda Ave.
Santa Rosa, Calif. 95404   *C*

Fred Meyer of California
1499 Potrero Ave.
San Francisco, Calif. 94110   *D*

Northwest Tube & Metal Fabricators
P.O. Box 02214
Portland, Ore. 97202   *C*

Robert H. Peterson Co.
2835 Sierra Grande St.
Pasadena, Calif. 91107   *H*

Portland Willamette Co.
6802 N.E. 59th Place
Portland, Ore. 97218   *D*

Preway, Inc.
Wisconsin Rapids, Wis. 54494   *C*

Rangaire Corp.
P.O. Box 177
Cleburne, Tex. 76031   *G*

Readybuilt Products Co.
1701 McHenry St.
Baltimore, Md. 21223   *F, G*

Royal-De Soto
Judd Road
Chattanooga, Tenn. 37406   *D, G*

Seymour Manufacturing Co.
Seymour, Ind. 47274   D

Superior Fireplace Co.
4325 Artesia Ave.
Fullerton, Calif. 92633   A, B, D, E, G, H, I

Tamro Industries, Inc.
2347 28th St. SE
Grand Rapids, Mich. 49506   D, Grate Heater

Temco, Inc.
4101 Charlotte Ave.
Nashville, Tenn. 37202   H

Thermo-Rite Mfg. Co.
Box 1108
Akron, Ohio 44309   C, D

United States Stove Co.
South Pittsburg, Tenn.   C

Vestal Manufacturing Co.
Box 420
Sweetwater, Tenn. 37874   A, C

Washington Stove Works
P.O. Box 687
Everett, Wash. 98201   C

CODE
A—Metal Parts for Fireplaces
B—Pre-Built Fireplaces, Flues
C—Metal Fireplaces
D—Fireplace Furnishings
E—Barbecue Equipment
F—Mantels
G—Electric Fireplaces
H—Gas Fireplaces
I—Circulating Fireplaces